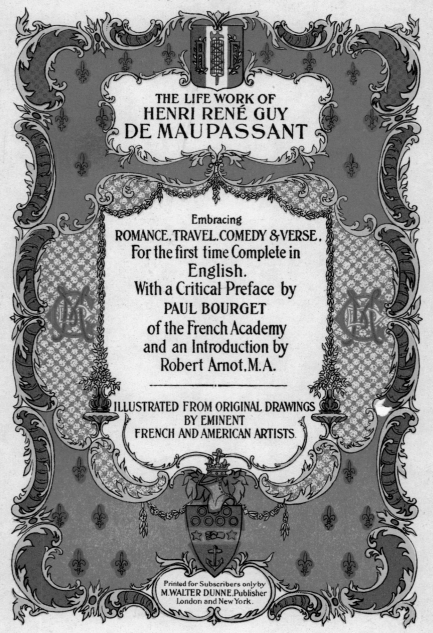

THE LIFE WORK OF
HENRI RENÉ GUY
DE MAUPASSANT

Embracing
ROMANCE. TRAVEL. COMEDY & VERSE.
For the first time Complete in
English.
With a Critical Preface by
PAUL BOURGET
of the French Academy
and an Introduction by
Robert Arnot, M.A.

ILLUSTRATED FROM ORIGINAL DRAWINGS
BY EMINENT
FRENCH AND AMERICAN ARTISTS.

Printed for Subscribers only by
M. WALTER DUNNE, Publisher
London and New York.

LA PAIX DU MÉNAGE

OR

A COMEDY OF MARRIAGE

IN TWO ACTS

BY

GUY DE MAUPASSANT

PRODUCED AT THE COMÉDIE FRANÇAISE IN 1893

VOL. XIV

M. WALTER DUNNE, PUBLISHER

NEW YORK AND LONDON

5324

TABLE OF CONTENTS

———

———

ADDENDA

ILLUSTRATIONS

_____

NO QUARTER

(xi)

LA PAIX DU MÉNAGE

DRAMATIS PERSONÆ

Monsieur de Sallus
Jacques de Randol
Madame de Sallus

Time: Paris, 1890

ACT I.

Scene I.

Mme. de Sallus *in her drawing-room, seated in a corner by the fireplace. Enter* Jacques de Randol *noiselessly; glances to see that no one is looking, and kisses* Mme. de Sallus *quickly upon her hair. She starts; utters a faint cry, and turns upon him.*

MME. DE SALLUS

Oh! How imprudent you are!

JACQUES DE RANDOL

Don't be afraid; no one saw me.

MME. DE SALLUS

But the servants!

JACQUES DE RANDOL

Oh, they are in the outer hall.

MME. DE SALLUS

How is that? No one announced you

JACQUES DE RANDOL

No, they simply opened the door for me.

(3)

MME. DE SALLUS

But what will *they* think?

JACQUES DE RANDOL

Well, they will doubtless think that *I* don't count.

MME. DE SALLUS

But I will not permit it. I must have you announced in future. It does not look well.

JACQUES DE RANDOL *[laughs]*

Perhaps they will even go so far as to announce your husband —

MME. DE SALLUS

Jacques, this jesting is out of place.

JACQUES DE RANDOL

Forgive me. [*Sits.*] Are you waiting for anybody?

MME. DE SALLUS

Yes — probably. You know that I always receive when I am at home.

JACQUES DE RANDOL

I know that I always have the pleasure of seeing you for about five minutes — just enough time to ask you how you feel, and then some one else comes in — some one in love with you, of course, — who impatiently awaits my departure.

MME. DE SALLUS [*smiles*]

Well, what can I do? I am not your wife, so how can it be otherwise?

JACQUES DE RANDOL

Ah! If you only were my wife!

MME. DE SALLUS

If I were your wife?

JACQUES DE RANDOL

I would snatch you away for five or six months, far from this horrible town, and keep you all to myself.

MME. DE SALLUS

You would soon have enough of me.

JACQUES DE RANDOL

No, no!

MME. DE SALLUS

Yes, yes!

JACQUES DE RANDOL

Do you know that it is absolute torture to love a woman like you?

MME. DE SALLUS [*bridles*]

And why?

JACQUES DE RANDOL

Because I covet you as the starving covet the food they see behind the glassy barriers of a restaurant.

MME. DE SALLUS

Oh, Jacques!

JACQUES DE RANDOL

I tell you it is true! A woman of the world belongs to the world; that is to say, to everyone except the man to whom she gives herself. He can see her with open doors for a quarter of an hour every three days — not oftener, because of servants. In exceptional cases, with a thousand precautions, with a thousand fears, with a thousand subterfuges, she visits him once or twice a month, perhaps, in a furnished room. Then she has just a quarter of an hour to give him, because she has just left Madame X in order to visit Madame Z, where she has told her coachman to take her. If he complains, she will not come again, because it is impossible for her to get rid of her coachman. So, you see, the coachman, and the footman, and Madame Z, and Madame X, and all the others, who visit her house as they would a museum, — a museum that never closes, — all the he's and all the she's who eat up her leisure minute by minute and second by second, to whom she owes her time as an employee owes his time to the State, simply because she belongs to the world — all these persons are like the transparent and impassable glass: they keep you from my love.

MME. DE SALLUS [*dryly*]

You seem upset to-day.

JACQUES DE RANDOL

No, no, but I hunger to be alone with you. You are mine, are you not? Or, I should say, I am yours. Isn't it true? I spend my life in looking for opportunities to meet you. Our love is made up of chance meetings, of casual bows, of stolen looks, of slight touches — nothing more. We meet on the avenue in the morning — a bow; we meet at your house, or at that of some other acquaintance — twenty words; we dine somewhere at the same table, too far from each

other to talk, and I dare not even look at you because of hostile eyes. Is that love? We are simply
acquaintances.

MME. DE SALLUS

Then you would like to carry me off?

JACQUES DE RANDOL

Unhappily, I cannot.

MME. DE SALLUS

Then what?

JACQUES DE RANDOL

I do not know. I only know this life is wearing
me out.

MME. DE SALLUS

It is just because there are so many obstacles in
the way of your love that it does not fade.

JACQUES DE RANDOL

Oh! Madeline, can you say that?

MME. DE SALLUS [*softening*]

Believe me, dear, if your love has to endure these
hardships, it is because it is not lawful love.

JACQUES DE RANDOL

Well, I never met a woman as positive as you.
Then you think that if chance made me your husband, I should cease to love you?

MME. DE SALLUS

Not all at once, perhaps, but — eventually.

JACQUES DE RANDOL

What you say is revolting to me.

MME. DE SALLUS

Nevertheless, it is quite true. You know that when a confectioner hires a greedy saleswoman he says to her, "Eat all the sweets you wish, my dear." She stuffs herself for eight days, and then she is satisfied for the rest of her life.

JACQUES DE RANDOL

Ah! Indeed! But why do you include me in that class?

MME. DE SALLUS

Really, I do not know—perhaps as a joke!

JACQUES DE RANDOL

Please do not mock me.

MME. DE SALLUS

I say to myself, here is a man who is very much in love with me. So far as I am concerned, I am perfectly free, morally, since for two years past I have altogether ceased to please my husband. Now, since this man loves me, why should I not love him?

JACQUES DE RANDOL

You are philosophic—and cruel.

MME. DE SALLUS

On the contrary, I have *not* been cruel. Of what do you complain?

JACQUES DE RANDOL

Stop! you anger me with this continual raillery. Ever since I began to love you, you have tortured me in this manner, and now I do not even know whether you have the slightest affection for me.

MME. DE SALLUS

Well, you must admit that I have always been — good-natured.

JACQUES DE RANDOL

Oh, you have played a queer little game! From the day I first met you I felt that you were coquetting with me, coquetting mysteriously, obscurely, coquetting as only you can without showing it to others. Little by little you conquered me with looks, with smiles, with pressures of the hand, without compromising yourself, without pledging yourself, without revealing yourself. You have been horribly upright — and seductive. I have loved you with all my soul, yes, sincerely and loyally, and to-day I do not know what feeling you have in the depths of your heart, what thoughts you have hidden in your brain; in fact, I know — I know nothing. I look at you, and I see a woman who seems to have chosen me, and seems also to have forgotten that she *has* chosen me. Does she love me, or is she tired of me? Has she simply made an experiment — taken a lover in order to see, to know, to taste, — without desire, hunger, or thirst? There are days when I ask myself if among those who love you and who tell you so unceasingly there is not one whom you really love.

MME. DE SALLUS

Good heavens! Really, there are *some* things into which it is not necessary to inquire.

JACQUES DE RANDOL

Oh, how hard you are! Your tone tells me that you do not love me.

MME. DE SALLUS

Now, what *are* you complaining about? Of things I do not say?—because—I do not think you have anything else to reproach me with.

JACQUES DE RANDOL

Forgive me, I am jealous.

MME. DE SALLUS

Of whom?

JACQUES DE RANDOL

I do not know. I am jealous of everything that I do not know about you.

MME. DE SALLUS

Yes, and without my knowing anything about these things, too.

JACQUES DE RANDOL

Forgive me, I love you too much—so much that everything disturbs me.

MME. DE SALLUS

Everything?

JACQUES DE RANDOL

Yes, everything.

MME. DE SALLUS

Are you jealous of my husband?

JACQUES DE RANDOL [*amazed*]

What an idea!

MME. DE SALLUS [*dryly*]

Well, you are wrong.

JACQUES DE RANDOL

Always this raillery!

MME. DE SALLUS

No, I want to speak to you seriously about him, and to ask your advice.

JACQUES DE RANDOL

About your husband?

MME. DE SALLUS [*seriously*]

Yes, I am not laughing, or rather I do not laugh any more. [*In lighter tone.*] Then you are not jealous of my husband? And yet you know he is the only man who has authority over me.

JACQUES DE RANDOL

It is just because he has authority that I am not jealous. A woman's heart gives nothing to the man who has authority.

MME. DE SALLUS

My dear, a husband's right is a positive thing; it is a title-deed that he can lock up—just as my husband has for more than two years—but it is also one

that he can use at any given moment, as lately he
has seemed inclined to do.

JACQUES DE RANDOL [*astonished*]

You tell me that your husband—

MME. DE SALLUS

Yes.

JACQUES DE RANDOL

Impossible!

MME. DE SALLUS [*bridles*]

And why impossible?

JACQUES DE RANDOL

Because your husband has—has—other occupations.

MME. DE SALLUS

Well, it pleases him to vary them, it seems.

JACQUES DE RANDOL

Jesting apart, Madeline, what has happened?

MME. DE SALLUS

Ah! Ah! Then you *are* becoming jealous of him.

JACQUES DE RANDOL

Madeline, I implore you; tell me, are you mocking
me, or are you speaking seriously?

MME. DE SALLUS

I am speaking seriously, indeed, very seriously.

JACQUES DE RANDOL

Then what has happened?

MME. DE SALLUS

Well, you know my position, although I have
never told you all my past life. It is all very simple
and very brief. At the age of nineteen I married the
Count de Sallus, who fell in love with me after he
had seen me at the Opéra-Comique. He already
knew my father's lawyer. He was very nice to me
in those early days; yes, very nice, and I really believed he loved me. As for myself, I was very circumspect in my behavior toward him, very circumspect
indeed, so that he could never cast a shadow of reproach on my name.

JACQUES DE RANDOL

Well, did you love him?

MME. DE SALLUS

Good gracious! Why ask such questions?

JACQUES DE RANDOL

Then you did love him?

MME. DE SALLUS

Yes and no. If I loved him, it was the love of a
little fool; but I certainly never told him, for posi-
tively I do not know how to show love.

JACQUES DE RANDOL

I can vouch for that!

MME. DE SALLUS

Well, it is possible that I cared for him sometimes, idiotically, like a timid, restless, trembling, awk-

ward, little girl, always in fear of that disturbing thing — the love of a man — that disturbing thing that is sometimes so sweet! As for him, — you know him. He was a sweetheart, a society sweetheart, who are always the worst of all. Such men really have a lasting affection only for those girls who are fitting companions for clubmen — girls who have a habit of telling doubtful stories and bestowing depraved kisses. It seems to me that to attract and to hold such people, the nude and obscene are necessary both in word and in body — unless — unless — it is true that men are incapable of loving any woman for a length of time.

However, I soon became aware that he was indifferent to me, for he used to kiss me as a matter of course and look at me without realizing my presence; and in his manners, in his actions, in his conversation, he showed that I attracted him no longer. As soon as he came into the room he would throw himself upon the sofa, take up the newspaper, read it, shrug his shoulders, and when he read anything he did not agree with, he would express his annoyance audibly. Finally, one day, he yawned and stretched his arms in my face. On that day I understood that I was no longer loved. Keenly mortified I certainly was. But it hurt me so much that I did not realize it was necessary to coquet with him in order to retain his affection. I soon learned that he had a mistress, a woman of the world. Since then we have lived separate lives — after a very stormy explanation.

JACQUES DE RANDOL

What do you mean? What sort of explanation?

MME. DE SALLUS

Well —

JACQUES DE RANDOL

About — his mistress?

MME. DE SALLUS

Yes and no. I find it difficult to express myself. To avoid my suspicions he found himself obliged, doubtless, to dissimulate from time to time, although rarely, and to feign a certain affection for his legitimate wife, the woman who had the right to his affection. I told him that he might abstain in future from such a mockery of love.

JACQUES DE RANDOL

How did you tell him that?

MME. DE SALLUS

I don't remember.

JACQUES DE RANDOL

It must have been amusing.

MME. DE SALLUS

No, he appeared very much surprised at first. Then I formulated a nice little speech and learned it by heart, in which I asked him to carry such intermittent fancies elsewhere. He understood me, saluted me very courteously, and — did as I asked him.

JACQUES DE RANDOL

Did he never come back?

MME. DE SALLUS

Never, until —

JACQUES DE RANDOL [*interrupts*]

Has he never again tried to tell you of his love?

MME. DE SALLUS

No, never, until —

JACQUES DE RANDOL [*interrupts*]

Have you regretted it?

MME. DE SALLUS

That is of small importance. What is of importance, though, is that he has had innumerable mistresses whom he entertains, whom he supports, whom he takes out. It is this that has irritated and humiliated me — in fact, cut me to the quick. But then I took heart of grace, and too late, two years too late, I took a lover — you!

JACQUES DE RANDOL [*kisses her hand*]

And I, Madeline, I love you with my whole soul.

MME. DE SALLUS

Well, all this is not at all proper.

JACQUES DE RANDOL

What do you mean by "all this"?

MME. DE SALLUS

Life in general — my husband — his mistresses — myself — and you.

JACQUES DE RANDOL

Your words prove beyond a doubt that you do not love me.

MME. DE SALLUS

Why?

JACQUES DE RANDOL

You dare to say of love that it is not proper? If you loved me, it might be divine, but a loving woman would abhor a phrase which should contain such an idea. What! True love not proper?

MME. DE SALLUS

Possibly. It all depends upon the point of view. For myself, I see too much.

JACQUES DE RANDOL

What do you see?

MME. DE SALLUS

I see too well, too far, too clearly.

JACQUES DE RANDOL

You do not love me?

MME. DE SALLUS

If I did not love you — a little — I should have had no excuse for giving myself to you.

JACQUES DE RANDOL

A little — just sufficient to warrant that excuse!

MME. DE SALLUS

But I do not excuse myself: I accuse myself.

14   G. de M.—2

JACQUES DE RANDOL

Then you did love me a little — and then — now — you love me no more!

MME. DE SALLUS

Do not let us argue.

JACQUES DE RANDOL

You do nothing else.

MME. DE SALLUS

No, I only judge the present by the past; the only just ideas and sane notions of life one can form are those concerning that which is past.

JACQUES DE RANDOL

And do you regret —

MME. DE SALLUS

Perhaps!

JACQUES DE RANDOL

And what about to-morrow?

MME. DE SALLUS

I do not know.

JACQUES DE RANDOL

Is it nothing to you to have one who is yours, body and soul?

MME. DE SALLUS [*shrugs her shoulders*]

Yes, mine to-day.

JACQUES DE RANDOL [*vehemently*]

And to-morrow!

MME. DE SALLUS [*shrugs her shoulders again*]

Yes, the to-morrow that follows to-night, but not the to-morrow of a year hence.

JACQUES DE RANDOL [*emphatically*]

You shall see.   But how about your husband?

MME. DE SALLUS

Does he annoy you?

JACQUES DE RANDOL

By heaven —

MME. DE SALLUS

Hush! [*Archly.*] My husband has fallen in love with me again.

JACQUES DE RANDOL

Is it possible?

MME. DE SALLUS [*indignantly*]

What do you mean by such an insolent question, and why should it not be possible?

JACQUES DE RANDOL

A man falls in love with his wife before he marries her, but after marriage he never commits the same mistake.

MME. DE SALLUS

But perhaps he has never really been in love with me until now.

JACQUES DE RANDOL

It is absolutely impossible that he could have lived with you — even in his curt, cavalier fashion — without loving you.

MME. DE SALLUS [*indifferently*]

It is of little importance. He has either loved me in the past, or is now beginning to love me.

JACQUES DE RANDOL

Truly, I do not understand you. Tell me all about it.

MME. DE SALLUS

But I have nothing to tell. He declares his love for me, takes me in his arms, and threatens me with his conjugal rights. This upsets me, torments me, and annoys me.

JACQUES DE RANDOL

Madeline you torture me.

MME. DE SALLUS [*quickly*]

And what about me? Do you think that I do not suffer? I know that I am not exactly a faithful woman since I received your addresses, but I have, and shall retain, a single heart. It is either you *or* he. It will never be you *and* he. For me that would be infamy — the greatest infamy of a guilty woman, the sharing of her heart — a thing that debases her. One may fall, perhaps, because there are ditches along the wayside and it is not always easy to follow the right path. But if one falls, that is no reason to throw oneself in the abyss.

JACQUES DE RANDOL [*takes her in his arms and kisses
her*]

I simply adore you!

MME. DE SALLUS [*melts*]

And I, too, love you dearly, Jacques, and that is
the reason why I fear.

JACQUES DE RANDOL

But, tell me, Madeline how long has it been since
your husband reformed?

MME. DE SALLUS

Possibly fifteen days or three weeks.

JACQUES DE RANDOL

Without relapse?

MME. DE SALLUS

Without relapse.

JACQUES DE RANDOL

I will explain the mystery. The fact of the matter is this, your husband has simply become a
widower.

MME. DE SALLUS

What do you say?

JACQUES DE RANDOL

I mean that your husband is unattached just now,
and seeks to spend his leisure time with his wife.

MME. DE SALLUS

But I tell you that he is in love with me.

JACQUES DE RANDOL

Yes — yes — and no. He is in love with you —
and also with another. Tell me, his temper is usually bad, isn't it?

MME. DE SALLUS

Execrable!

JACQUES DE RANDOL

Well, then, here is a man in love with you who
shows his wonderful return of tenderness by moods
that are simply unsupportable — for they are unsupportable, aren't they?

MME. DE SALLUS

Absolutely.

JACQUES DE RANDOL

If he wooed you with tenderness you would not
feel fear. You would say to yourself, "My turn has
come at last," and then he would inspire you with a
little pity for him, for a woman has always a sneak-
ing sort of compassion for the man who loves her,
even though that man be her husband.

MME. DE SALLUS

Perhaps that is true.

JACQUES DE RANDOL

Is he nervous, preoccupied?

MME. DE SALLUS

Yes.

JACQUES DE RANDOL

And he is abrupt with you, not to say brutal?
He demands his right without even praying for it?

MME. DE SALLUS

True.

JACQUES DE RANDOL

My darling, for the moment you are simply a substitute.

MME. DE SALLUS

Oh! no, no!

JACQUES DE RANDOL

My dearest girl, your husband's latest mistress was Madame de Bardane, whom he left very abruptly about two months ago to run after the Santelli.

MME. DE SALLUS

What, the singer?

JACQUES DE RANDOL

Yes, a capricious, saucy, cunning, venal little woman. A woman not at all uncommon upon the stage, or in the world either, for that matter.

MME. DE SALLUS

Then that is why he haunts the Opéra.

JACQUES DE RANDOL [*laughs*]

Without a doubt.

MME. DE SALLUS [*dreamily*]

No, no, you are deceiving yourself.

JACQUES DE RANDOL [*emphatically*]

The Santelli resists him and repulses him; then, burdened with a heart full of longing that has no outlet, he deigns to offer you a portion.

MME. DE SALLUS

My dear, you are dreaming. If he were in love with the Santelli, he would not tell me that he loves me. If he were so entirely preoccupied with this creature, he would not woo me. If he coveted her, he would not desire me at the same time.

JACQUES DE RANDOL

How little you understand certain kinds of men! Men like your husband, once inoculated with the poison of love,— which in them is nothing but brutal desire,— men like him, I say, when a woman they desire escapes or resists them, become raging beasts. They behave like madmen, like men possessed, with arms outstretched and lips wide open. They must love some one, no matter whom just as a mad dog with open jaws bites anything and everybody. The Santelli has unchained this raging brute, and you find yourself face to face with his dripping jaws. Take care! You call that love! It is nothing but animal passion.

MME. DE SALLUS [*sarcastically*]

Really, you are very unfair to him. I am afraid jealousy is blinding you.

JACQUES DE RANDOL

Oh, no, I am not deceiving myself, you may be sure.

MME. DE SALLUS

Yes, I think you are. Formerly my husband neglected and abandoned me, doubtless finding me very insipid; but now he finds me much improved, and has returned to me. It is very easy to understand, and moreover, it is the worse for him, for he *must* believe that I have been a *faithful* wife to him all my life.

JACQUES DE RANDOL

Madeline!

MME. DE SALLUS

Well, what?

JACQUES DE RANDOL

Does a girl cease to be a faithful wife, if, when deserted by the man who has assumed charge of her existence, and her happiness, and her love, and her ideals, she refuses to resign herself — young, beautiful, and full of hope — to eternal isolation and everlasting solitude?

MME. DE SALLUS

I think I have already told you that there are certain things which it is *not* necessary to discuss, and this is one of them. [*The front door bell sounds twice.*] Here is my husband. Please be silent. He is in a gloomy mood just now.

JACQUES DE RANDOL [*rises*]

I think I shall go. I am not in love with your husband any more, for many reasons, and it is difficult for me to be polite to him when I despise him, and when I know that he ought to despise me, and would despise me when I shake hands with him, did he know all.

MME. DE SALLUS [*annoyed*]

How many times must I tell you that all this is entirely out of place?

Scene II.

(*The same, including* M. de Sallus.)

Enter M. de Sallus, *evidently in a bad temper. He looks for a moment at* Mme. de Sallus *and at* Jacques de Randol, *who is taking his leave; then comes forward.*

JACQUES DE RANDOL

Ah! Sallus.

M. DE SALLUS

How are you, Randol? Surely you are not going because I came.

JACQUES DE RANDOL

No, but my time is up. I have an appointment at the club at midnight, and now it is half after eleven. [*They shake hands.*] Have you come from the first performance of "Mahomet"?

M. DE SALLUS

Oh! Of course.

JACQUES DE RANDOL

People say that it should be a great success.

M. DE SALLUS

It doubtless will be.

JACQUES DE RANDOL [*shakes hands again with* De Sallus *and* Madame de Sallus]

Well, till I see you again.

M. DE SALLUS

Till then, my dear fellow.

JACQUES DE RANDOL

Madame, adieu.

MME. DE SALLUS

Adieu, Monsieur de Randol.　　　[*Exit* Randol.

SCENE III.

(M. de Sallus *and* Mme. de Sallus.)

M. DE SALLUS [*sinks into an armchair*]

Was Randol here any length of time?

MME. DE SALLUS

No, possibly half an hour.

M. DE SALLUS [*meditatively*]

Half an hour plus a whole hour makes an hour
and a half, does it not? Time seems to fly when
you are with him.

MME. DE SALLUS

What do you mean by an hour and a half?

M. DE SALLUS

Just what I say. When I saw the carriage waiting at the door, I asked the footman who was within.
He told me that it was M. Jacques de Randol. "Has
he been here long?" I asked. "He has been here

since ten," said the footman.   Admitting that the man might have been mistaken, we will say, in the matter of a quarter of an hour, that would make an hour and a quarter, at the least.

MME. DE SALLUS

Oh, ho! What is this new attitude of yours? Have I not a right to receive whom I like now?

M. DE SALLUS

Oh, my dear, I deny you nothing, nothing, nothing. The only thing that astonishes me is that you do not know the difference between half an hour and an hour and a half.

MME. DE SALLUS

Are you looking for a scene? If you wish a quarrel, say so. I shall know how to answer you. You are simply in a bad temper. Go to bed and sleep, if you can.

M. DE SALLUS

I am not looking for a quarrel, neither am I in bad humor. I only state that time flies with you when you pass it in the company of Jacques de Randol.

MME. DE SALLUS

Yes, it does go quickly; far more quickly than when I am with you.

M. DE SALLUS

He is a very charming fellow, and I know you like him; and, moreover, he must like you very much, since he comes here every day.

MME. DE SALLUS

These insinuations are distasteful to me. Please speak plainly and say what you mean. Are you assuming the rôle of a jealous husband?

M. DE SALLUS

God forbid! I have too much confidence in you, and far too much esteem for you, to reproach you with anything, for I know that you have too much tact ever to give rise to calumny or scandal.

MME. DE SALLUS

Do not play with words. You think that M. Jacques de Randol comes too often to this house — to your house?

M. DE SALLUS

I do not find any fault with you for that.

MME. DE SALLUS

Thank you. You simply have not the right. However, since you adopt this attitude, let us settle this question once for all, for I loathe misunderstandings. It seems to me that you have an exceedingly short memory. Let me come to your aid. Be frank with me. Through some occurrence, the nature of which I do not know, your attitude is different to-day from that of the past two years. Cast your memory over the past, to the time when you began to neglect me in a manner that was plain to all. I became very uneasy. Then I knew — I was told, and I saw — that you were in love with Madame de Servières. I told you how hurt I was, how grieved I was. What did you reply? Just what every

man replies when he no longer loves the woman
who reproaches him.   You shrugged your shoulders,
smiled impatiently, told me I was mad, and then ex-
pounded to me — I must admit, in a most skillful
manner — those grand principles of freedom in love
that are adopted by every husband who deceives his
wife and thinks she will not deceive him.   You gave
me to understand that marriage is not a bond, but
simply an association of mutual interests, a social
rather than a moral alliance; that it does not demand
friendship or affection between married couples, provided there be no scandal.   You did not absolutely
confess the existence of your mistresses, but you
pleaded extenuating circumstances.   You were very
sarcastic upon the subject of those poor, silly women
who object to their husbands being gallant toward
other women, since, according to you, such gallantry
is one of the laws of the polished society to which
you belong.   You laughed at the foolish man who
does not dare to pay compliments to a woman in
the presence of his own wife, and ridiculed the
gloomy look of a wife whose eyes follow her husband into every corner, imagining that because the
poor man disappears into an adjoining room he is at
the feet of a rival.   All this was very airy, funny,
and disagreeable, wrapped up in compliments and
spiced with cynicism — sweet and bitter at the same
time, and calculated to banish from the heart all love
for a smooth, false, and well-bred man who could
talk in such a manner.   I understood, I wept, I suffered, and then I shut my door upon you.   You
made no objection; you judged me better than you
thought; and since then we have lived completely

separate lives. Such has been the case for the past two years, two long years and more, which certainly have not seemed more than six months to you. We go into society as usual, we return from society as usual, and we each enter our own temple of life. The situation was established by you in consequence of your first infidelity, an infidelity which has been followed by many others. I have said nothing; I have resigned myself to the situation; and I have banished you from my heart. Now that I have finished, what do you wish?

M. DE SALLUS

My dear, I am not asking for anything. I do not even wish to answer the very aggressive speech you have done me the honor to make. I only wish to give you advice — the advice of a friend — upon a situation that may possibly endanger your reputation. You are beautiful, always in the public eye, and much envied. Scandal could have easy birth.

MME. DE SALLUS

Pardon me. If we are to speak of scandal, I must have leave to balance my account with you.

M. DE SALLUS

Come, do not let us joke over this thing. I speak to you as a friend — seriously, as a friend. As to what you have said about me, it is all extremely exaggerated.

MME. DE SALLUS

Not at all. You have never tried to conceal, in fact, you have actually proclaimed to all the world your infidelities — a fact which gives me the right to go and do likewise, and, my friend, believe what I say —

M. DE SALLUS

One moment —

MME. DE SALLUS

Let me finish. According to you, I am beautiful, I am young, and yet condemned by my husband to live, and watch him live, as if I were a widow. Look at me [*rises*], is it just to consign me to play the rôle of an abandoned Ariadne, while my husband runs from this woman to that woman, and this girl to that girl? [*Grows excited.*] A faithful wife! I cry you mercy! Is a faithful wife compelled to sacrifice all her life, all her happiness, all her affections, everything, in fact, every privilege, every expectation, every claim, which is hers by birth and for which she has been born? Look at me! Am I made for a nunnery? The fact that I married you should answer that question. And yet, you, *you,* who took me from my father's house, neglect me to run after others. And what others? I am not in their circle, neither am I one of those who would share your life with others. So much the worse for you — for I am free, and you have no right to give me advice since I *am* free.

M. DE SALLUS

My dear girl, be calm. You misunderstand me completely. I have never suspected you. Indeed, I have the most profound esteem and friendship for you — a loving friendship which grows greater every day. I have no wish to comment upon that past with which you reproach me so cruelly.   Perhaps I am a little too—too—what shall I say?

MME. DE SALLUS

Oh! Say that you belong to the period of the Regency.   I know that method of excusing all male weaknesses and follies.   Oh! yes; that eighteenth century, that *dainty* century, so full of *elegance,* so full of delicious *fantasies* and adorable *whims!* Alas! my dear, that is ancient history.

M. DE SALLUS

No, no, you misunderstand me again.   Believe me, I am and have been above everything too—too—much of a Parisian, too much accustomed to turning night into day, for the sedate life of marriage.   I have been too much accustomed to go behind the scenes of theaters, to various clubs, to a thousand other forms of dissipation; and you know a man cannot change all at once,—it takes time.   Marriage seeks to change us all too suddenly.   It ought to give us time to get accustomed to it, little by little.   You would practically take away from me the joy of life were I to behave as you seem to desire.

MME. DE SALLUS

I am so grateful; and now, perhaps, you wish to offer me a new proof—a new proof—

M. DE SALLUS

Oh, as you please.   Really, when a man who has lived as I have marries, he can hardly help looking upon his wife as a new mistress—I mean to say a faithful mistress — and it is only when it is too late that he understands more clearly, — comes to his senses and repents.

MME. DE SALLUS

Well, my friend, it *is* too late. As I have already told you, I mean to have my innings. I have taken nearly three years to think it over. You may think that is long, but I need some amusement as well as you. The fact that I have taken nearly three years to think it over is a compliment to you, but you fail to see it.

M. DE SALLUS

Madeline, this jesting is altogether out of place.

MME. DE SALLUS

Oh! no, because I am compelled to think that every one of your mistresses was far more attractive than I, since you have preferred them to me.

M. DE SALLUS

What sort of mood are you in?

MME. DE SALLUS

In the same mood that I always am. It is you who have changed.

M. DE SALLUS

True, I *have* changed.

MME. DE SALLUS

And that is to say —

M. DE SALLUS

That I have been an idiot.

MME. DE SALLUS

And that —

M. DE SALLUS

I am sane once more.

MME. DE SALLUS

And that —

M. DE SALLUS

That I am again in love with my wife.

MME. DE SALLUS

You must have returned to your youth.

M. DE SALLUS

What do you say?

MME. DE SALLUS

I say that you must have returned to your youth.

M. DE SALLUS

What do you mean?

MME. DE SALLUS

Let me illustrate. When you are young you are always hungry, and when a youth is hungry he often eats things that he would not eat at another time. Well, I am the dish,—the dish that you have neglected in your days of plenty, the dish to which you return in the days of scarcity—[*slowly*] for which I thank you!

M. DE SALLUS

I have never looked upon you as you think. You pain me as well as astonish me.

MME. DE SALLUS

So much the worse for both of us. If I astonish you, you repel me. Learn now, once for all, that I am not made for the rôle of a substitute.

M. DE SALLUS [*approaches her, takes her hand and presses a long kiss upon it*]

Madeline, I swear to you that I love you, in truth, devotedly, now and forever.

MME. DE SALLUS [*ironically*]

You must really believe it! [*Suddenly.*] But who is the woman that attracts — and repels you — just now?

M. DE SALLUS

Madeline, I swear —

MME. DE SALLUS

Oh, a truce to your swearing! I know that you have just broken with one of your mistresses; you need another and you cannot find one, so you come to me. For nearly three years you have forgotten all about me, so that now you find I am somewhat of a novelty. It is not your wife you are seeking now, but a woman with whom you have formerly had a rupture, and with whom you now desire to make up. To speak the truth you are simply playing the game of a libertine.

M. DE SALLUS

I do not ask you whether you be my wife or not my wife. You are the woman I love, the woman who possesses my heart. You are the woman of

whom I dream, whose image follows me everywhere,
whom I continually desire. It happens that you are
my wife. So much the worse, or so much the better. What matters it?

MME. DE SALLUS

Truly, it is a distinguished part that you offer me.
After Mademoiselle Zozo, after Mademoiselle Lilie,
Mademoiselle Tata, you have the audacity to offer to
your wife — to Madame de Sallus — the place left vacant, asking her to become her husband's mistress
for a short space of time.

M. DE SALLUS

No; now, and — forever.

MME. DE SALLUS

Pardon me. You ask that I should re-become
your wife forever? That is out of the question; I
have already ceased to entertain the idea. The reason
may be obscure, but nevertheless it is real; and after
all, the idea of making me your *legitimate* mistress
seems to be far more entertaining to you than assuming the rôle of a *faithful* husband.

M. DE SALLUS [*laughs*]

Well, why should not the wife become the husband's mistress? You are right in what you say;
you are absolutely free and I own my faults. Yet, I
am in love with you — for the second time, if you
will — and I say to you, here and now, Madeline,
since you confess that your heart is empty, have
pity upon me, for I tell you that I love you.

MME. DE SALLUS

And you ask me to give you a husband's right?

M. DE SALLUS

I do.

MME. DE SALLUS

And you acknowledge that I am free, absolutely free?

M. DE SALLUS

I do.

MME. DE SALLUS

And you really wish me to become your mistress?

M. DE SALLUS

I do.

MME. DE SALLUS

You understand what I mean — your mistress?

M. DE SALLUS

Yes.

MME. DE SALLUS [*sarcastically*]

Well, well! I think I would rather accept another offer that I have, but since you are good enough to ask me to give you the preference, I may give it to you — for a fair sum.

M. DE SALLUS

What do you mean?

MME. DE SALLUS

Just what I say. Listen! Do you consider me as attractive as any of your mistresses? Now, be frank with me.

M. DE SALLUS

A thousand times more!

MME. DE SALLUS

Really!

M. DE SALLUS

I swear it!

MME. DE SALLUS

What, better than the best?

M. DE SALLUS

A thousand times!

MME. DE SALLUS

Well, tell me, now, truly, how much has the one you liked best among all your numerous mistresses cost you, let us say — in three months?

M. DE SALLUS

I cannot tell.

MME. DE SALLUS

Listen to me. I repeat the question. How much has the most charming of your numerous mistresses cost you in the space of three months — not only in money, but in gifts of jewelry, in dainty little suppers, in ceremonious dinners, in theater boxes, — in everything?

M. DE SALLUS

How can I tell?

MME. DE SALLUS

You should be able to. Come, let us make an estimate. Did you give her a round sum, or did you pay for everything separately? However, I know you

are not a man to bother over details, so I conclude
that you gave her a round sum.

M. DE SALLUS

Madeline, you are absolutely unbearable.

MME. DE SALLUS

Follow me closely. When you began to neglect
me, you took away three horses from our stables—
one of them was mine and the other two were yours.
Then you took away a coachman and a footman; you
then found it necessary to make me economize at
home in order that you might be extravagant abroad.

M. DE SALLUS

That is not true.

MME. DE SALLUS

Oh! yes, it is. I have every date; do not deny it,
for I shall confound you if you do. You also stopped
giving me jewels, for, of course, you had other ears,
other fingers, other wrists, and other necks to adorn.
You also deprived me of one of my nights at the Opéra,
and I do not know how many other things less important. And all this, according to my idea, should
mean about five thousand francs a month. Am I not
right?

M. DE SALLUS

You may be, but you are mad.

MME. DE SALLUS

No, no, confess; did the most expensive one of
your mistresses cost you about five thousand francs a
month?

M. DE SALLUS

You are crazy.

MME. DE SALLUS

If you are going to answer me thus, I bid you good evening. [*She rises as if to retire, but* M. de Sallus *interposes.*]

M. DE SALLUS

Come now, Madeline, a truce to this jesting.

MME. DE SALLUS [*in a determined manner*]

Five thousand francs? Tell me, did she cost you five thousand francs?

M. DE SALLUS [*shrugs his shoulders*]

Oh, yes, thereabouts.

MME. DE SALLUS [*looks him straight in the face*]

Ah, ah! Well, listen. If you will give me immediately five thousand francs, you may be my husband for a month — but only a month.

M. DE SALLUS

You have lost your head!

MME. DE SALLUS

Well, farewell, good night!

M. DE SALLUS

What a farce! Stop, Madeline, let us talk seriously.

MME. DE SALLUS

About what?

M. DE SALLUS

Of—of—hang it—of my love for you.

MME. DE SALLUS [*archly*]

But that's not a serious question at all.

M. DE SALLUS

I swear it is!

MME. DE SALLUS

Hypocrite! You make me thirsty with so much talk. [*Goes to a chiffonier, where there is a decanter and various liqueurs, and pours herself out a glass of water. At the instant she begins to drink, M. de Sallus steals up and kisses her on the back of the neck. She turns with a start and throws the glass of water in his face.*]

M. DE SALLUS

I suppose you think that funny.

MME. DE SALLUS

It may or may not be. Certainly what you have done, or tried to do, was ridiculous.

M. DE SALLUS

Madeline, I ask—

MME. DE SALLUS

Five—thousand—francs.

M. DE SALLUS

But that would be idiotic.

MME. DE SALLUS

And why?

M. DE SALLUS

Ask me why a husband should pay his wife — his lawful wife — when he has the right?

MME. DE SALLUS

Oh, no, no. You may have the strength, but I can have my revenge.

M. DE SALLUS

Madeline —

MME. DE SALLUS

Five — thousand — francs.

M. DE SALLUS

I should be an object of ridicule forever if I were to pay my wife — yes — not only an object of ridicule, but an idiot, an imbecile.

MME. DE SALLUS

Well, don't you think it is still more imbecile, when you have such a wife as I, to — to go outside and — pay mistresses?

M. DE SALLUS

Madeline, I confess it; but now — we are husband and wife, and it is not necessary to ruin me, is it?

MME. DE SALLUS

Allow me. When you took your wealth—the wealth which was also partly mine by marriage—to pay for your folly, you committed an action that was more than doubtful. In fact, it was criminal, for you ruined me at the same time you ruined yourself. I use your own language. I have refrained from asking you more about the folly that is in question; moreover, the five thousand francs that you must give me will be spent upon your own house. You must admit that is practical economy. But I know you; I know that you are never in love with anything that is lawful and right; so in paying dearly—very dearly, because I shall probably seek an increase—for what you have the right to take, you will find our— *liaison*—far more to your taste. [*Smiles.*] Good night, I am going to bed.

M. DE SALLUS [*angrily*]

Will you take it in cash, or have a cheque?

MME. DE SALLUS [*haughtily*]

I prefer cash.

M. DE SALLUS [*opening a pocketbook*]

I have only three bank-notes. I will give you the rest in a cheque. [*Writes a cheque and hands it to* Mme. de Sallus.]

MME. DE SALLUS [*takes the cheque, looks at* M. de Sallus *with disgust, and speaks in harsh tones*]

You are just the kind of man I took you to be. After paying your numerous mistresses, you actually

AFTER AN ORIGINAL DRAWING BY J. C. FIREMAN.

"Adieu, Monsieur."

(See page 45.)

consent to pay me as if I were like them — without
any feeling of disgust or realizing the difference in
our situation. You have said that I asked too much,
you have pleaded the fear of ridicule, but you could
not understand that you were consenting to *buy* me —
me — your *wife!* You wished to possess me for a
little, as a sort of variation to your usual list, although
your heart must have told you that it was degrading
to me to be placed on such a plane. You did not
recoil from such an idea, but pursued it, just as you
pursue them, and the more eagerly, because I was
more expensive. But you have deceived yourself, not
me. Not thus will you ever regain possession of
your wife. Adieu, Monsieur! [*Throws the money
in his face, and makes a haughty exit.*]

ACT II.

SCENE I.

Madame de Sallus *alone in her drawing-room, as in* Act I. *She is writing; she stops and looks at the clock. A servant announces* Monsieur Jacques de Randol.

JACQUES DE RANDOL [*after kissing* Mme. de Sallus's *hand*]

I TRUST you are well, Madame.

MME. DE SALLUS

Oh, yes, thank you.

[*Exit servant.*

JACQUES DE RANDOL

What is it all about? Your letter has completely upset me. I thought some accident had occurred, and I came immediately.

MME. DE SALLUS [*looks at him steadfastly*]

My dear Jacques, we must decide upon some course of action immediately. The important hour has come.

(46)

JACQUES DE RANDOL [*surprised*]

What do you mean?

MME. DE SALLUS

For two days I have undergone all the anguish that a woman's heart can endure.

JACQUES DE RANDOL [*still more surprised*]

What has happened?

MME. DE SALLUS ·

I am about to tell you, but I wish to do so with calmness and moderation lest you think me mad. That is the reason why I sent for you.

JACQUES DE RANDOL

You know that I am yours entirely. Tell me what I must do.

MME. DE SALLUS

I cannot live near him any longer. It is absolutely impossible. It is an hourly crucifixion.

JACQUES DE RANDOL

Near your husband?

MME. DE SALLUS

Yes, my husband.

JACQUES DE RANDOL

What has he done?

MME. DE SALLUS

It is necessary to revert to the other evening, after you took your leave. When we were alone he tried to make a jealous scene, with you as the subject.

JACQUES DE RANDOL

With me as the subject?

MME. DE SALLUS

Yes, a scene which proved to me that he had been watching us.

JACQUES DE RANDOL

How?

MME. DE SALLUS

He had been questioning a servant.

JACQUES DE RANDOL

Nothing more than that?

MME. DE SALLUS

No. That in itself, however, is not of much importance, for I believe he really likes you. But, after that, he told me of his love for me. Perhaps I was a little too insolent, too disdainful. I do not know exactly how far I went; but I found myself in such a perplexing, such a painful, such an extraordinary situation, that I dared everything to escape it.

JACQUES DE RANDOL

What did you do?

MME. DE SALLUS

I sought to wound him so deeply that he would leave me forever.

JACQUES DE RANDOL

Apparently you have not succeeded.

MME. DE SALLUS

No.

JACQUES DE RANDOL

Of course not; that method never does succeed. On the contrary, it often brings about a reconciliation.

MME. DE SALLUS

The next day, during luncheon, he was sulky, irritable, and gloomy. Then, as he was rising from the table, he said, "I have not forgotten your behavior of yesterday, and shall not let you forget it. You wish for war, let it be war; but I warn you that I shall conquer you, because I am your master." I answered him, "Be it so; but if you drive me to extremity, take care,—it is not always safe to make a woman desperate."

JACQUES DE RANDOL

Especially when that woman is his wife. And what did he reply?

MME. DE SALLUS

He did not reply in words; but he treated me brutally.

14 G. de M.—4

JACQUES DE RANDOL

Did he strike you?

MME. DE SALLUS

Yes and no. He jostled me, he squeezed me, he suffocated me. I have bruises all along my arms, but he did not strike me.

JACQUES DE RANDOL

Then what did he do?

MME. DE SALLUS

He hugged and embraced me, trying to overcome my resistance.

JACQUES DE RANDOL

Is that all?

MME. DE SALLUS

What do you mean by saying, "Is that all?" Don't you think that is enough?

JACQUES DE RANDOL

You do not understand me. I only wish to know whether he struck you.

MME. DE SALLUS

Oh, no. I am not afraid of that from him; but luckily I was able to ring the bell.

JACQUES DE RANDOL

You rang the bell?

MME. DE SALLUS

Yes.

JACQUES DE RANDOL

What a thing to do! [*Smiles.*] And when the servant came, did you ask him to show your husband out?

MME. DE SALLUS [*pouts*]

You seem to find this very funny.

JACQUES DE RANDOL

Oh, no, my dear Madame; it is all exceedingly painful to me, but I cannot help realizing the grotesqueness of the situation. Pardon me,—and what then?

MME. DE SALLUS

I ordered my carriage. And then, as soon as Joseph had gone out, my husband said, with that arrogant air which you know so well in him, "To-day, or to-morrow—it matters not which."

JACQUES DE RANDOL

And—

MME. DE SALLUS

And that is almost all.

JACQUES DE RANDOL

Almost?

MME. DE SALLUS

Yes, because since then I have locked myself in my room as soon as I heard him coming in.

JACQUES DE RANDOL

Haven't you seen him since?

MME. DE SALLUS

Oh, yes, several times, but only for a few minutes each time.

JACQUES DE RANDOL

What has he said to you?

MME. DE SALLUS

Little or nothing. He either sneers or insolently asks whether I am less savage to-day. Last night at the table he brought out a little book, which he read during dinner. As I did not wish to appear embarrassed or anxious, and desired to maintain my dignity, I said: "Your manners toward me are certainly exceedingly courteous." He smiled and replied: "What did you say?" "It is strange that, for reading, you should choose the time that we are together," I said. He answered: "Great heavens! It is all your fault, since you do not care to be amiable. Besides, this little book is very interesting. It is the Civil Code. Perhaps you would like to become acquainted with some clauses in it. They would certainly interest you." Then he read me the law concerning marriage; the duties of a wife and the rights of a husband. Then he looked me full in the face, and asked me whether I understood. I answered in the same tone that I understood too much,—especially did I understand the kind of man I had married. Then I went out and I have not seen him since.

JACQUES DE RANDOL

Haven't you seen him to-day?

MME. DE SALLUS

No. He lunched alone. As for myself, I have thought over the situation, and have decided not to meet him *tête-à-tête* any more.

JACQUES DE RANDOL

But are you quite sure that at bottom his attitude is not induced by anger, by wounded vanity, by disappointment, and perhaps by a little bravado? Possibly he will behave himself better in future. To-night he is at the Opéra. The Santelli has scored a great success in "Mahomet," and I think she has invited him to supper after the performance. Now, if the supper is very much to his taste, he will probably be in good humor when he comes home.

MME. DE SALLUS

Oh! How provoking you are. Can't you understand that I am in the power of this man, that I belong to him even more than his valet or his dog, because he has those abominable legal rights over me? The Code, your barbarous Code, puts me entirely in his power without any possible defense on my part; save actually killing me, he can do everything. Can't you understand that? Can't you realize the horror of my situation? Imagine, save actual murder, he can do anything to me, and he has the strength — not only physical but legal — to obtain anything from me. And I, I have not a single avenue of escape from a man whom I despise and hate. And that is the law made by you men! He took me, married me, deserted me. On my part, I have an absolutely moral right to leave him. And yet, despite this righteous hatred, this overpowering disgust, this loathing which creeps through me in the presence of the man who has scorned me, deceived me, and who has fluttered, right under my eyes, from girl to girl — this man, I say, has the right to demand from me a shameful and infamous concession. I have no right to hide myself; I have no right even to a key to my own door. Everything belongs to him — the key, the door, and even the woman who hates him. It is monstrous! Can you imagine such a horrible situation? That a woman should not be mistress of herself, should not even have the sacred right of preserving her person from a loathsome stain? And all this is the consequence of the infamous law which you men have made!

JACQUES DE RANDOL [appealingly]

My darling! I fully understand what you must be suffering; but how can I help it? No magistrate can protect you; no statute can preserve you.

MME. DE SALLUS

I know it. But when you have neither mother nor father to protect you, when the law is against you, and when you shrink from complicity in those degrading transactions to which many women yield themselves, there is always one means of escape.

JACQUES DE RANDOL

And that?

MME. DE SALLUS

Flight.

JACQUES DE RANDOL

You mean to say —

MME. DE SALLUS

Flight.

JACQUES DE RANDOL

Alone?

MME. DE SALLUS

No — with you.

JACQUES DE RANDOL

With me! Are you dreaming?

MME. DE SALLUS

No; so much the better. The scandal of it will prevent him from taking me back. I have gained courage now. Since he forces me to dishonor, I shall see that that dishonor is complete and over-whelming — even though it be the worse for him and for me.

JACQUES DE RANDOL

Oh! Beware, beware, my darling! You are in one of those moments of exaltation and nervous ex-citement in which a woman sometimes commits a folly that is irreparable.

MME. DE SALLUS

Well, I would rather commit such a folly and ruin myself — if that be ruin — than expose myself to the infamous struggle with which each day I am threatened.

JACQUES DE RANDOL

Madeline, hear me. You are in a terrible situation, but for God's sake do not throw yourself into one that is irretrievable. Be calm, I implore you.

MME. DE SALLUS

Well, what do you advise?

JACQUES DE RANDOL

I do not know; we shall see. But I do not, I cannot, advise you to venture on a scandal which will put you outside the pale of society.

MME. DE SALLUS

Well, yes, there is another law, an unwritten law which permits one to have lovers, even though it be shameful, because [*sarcastically*] it does not outrage society.

JACQUES DE RANDOL

That is not the question. The thing is to avoid taking up a wrong position in your quarrel with your husband. Have you decided to leave him?

MME. DE SALLUS

Yes.

JACQUES DE RANDOL

Finally and forever?

MME. DE SALLUS

Yes.

JACQUES DE RANDOL

Do you mean for *all* time?

MME. DE SALLUS

For *all* time.

JACQUES DE RANDOL

Well, now, be cautious; be careful and cunning; guard your reputation and your name. Make neither commotion nor scandal, and await your opportunity.

MME. DE SALLUS [*ironically*]

And must I continue to be very charming when he returns to me, and be ready for all his fancies?

JACQUES DE RANDOL

Oh, Madeline, I speak to you in the truest friendship.

MME. DE SALLUS [*bitterly*]

In the truest friendship!

JACQUES DE RANDOL

Yea, as a friend who loves you far too dearly to advise you to commit any folly.

MME. DE SALLUS

And loves me just enough to advise me to be complaisant to a man I despise.

JACQUES DE RANDOL

I! Never, never. My most ardent desire is to be with you forever. Get a divorce, and then if you still love me, let us wed.

MME. DE SALLUS

Oh, yes, yes — two years from now. Certainly, you *are* a patient lover!

JACQUES DE RANDOL

But supposing I were to carry you off, he would take you back to-morrow; would shut you up in his house, and would never get a divorce lest you should become my wife.

MME. DE SALLUS

Well, do you mean to say I could fly nowhere but to your house, that I could not hide myself in such fashion that he would never find me?

JACQUES DE RANDOL

Yes, you could hide yourself, but it would be necessary for you to live abroad under another name, or buried in the country, till death. That is the curse of our love. In three months you would hate me. I never will let you commit such a folly.

MME. DE SALLUS

I thought you loved me enough to fly with me, but it seems that I am mistaken. Adieu!

JACQUES DE RANDOL

Madeline, listen to me for God's —

MME. DE SALLUS

Jacques, take me, or leave me — answer!

JACQUES DE RANDOL

Madeline, I implore you!

MME. DE SALLUS

Never! Adieu! [*Rises and goes to the door.*]

JACQUES DE RANDOL

Once more I implore you, Madeline, listen to me.

MME. DE SALLUS

Oh, no, no; adieu! [De Randol *takes her by the arms; she frees herself angrily.*] Unhand me! Let me go, or I shall call for help!

JACQUES DE RANDOL

Call if you will, but listen to me. I would not that you should ever be able to reproach me for the madness that you meditate. God forbid that you should hate me, but, bound to me by this flight that you propose, you would carry with you forever a keen and unavailing regret that I allowed you to do it.

MME. DE SALLUS

Let me go! I despise you! Let me go!

JACQUES DE RANDOL

Well, if you wish to fly, why, let us fly.

MME. DE SALLUS

Oh, no, not now. I know you now. It is too late. Let me go.

JACQUES DE RANDOL

I have done exactly what I ought to have done; I have said exactly what I ought to have said; consequently, I am no longer responsible for you, and you have no right to reproach me with the consequences. So let us fly.

MME. DE SALLUS

Oh, no, it is too late, and I do not care to accept sacrifices.

JACQUES DE RANDOL

There is no more any question of sacrifice. To fly with you is my most ardent desire.

MME. DE SALLUS [*astonished*]

You are mad.

JACQUES DE RANDOL

Well, suppose I am mad. That is only natural, since I love you.

MME. DE SALLUS

What do you mean?

JACQUES DE RANDOL

I mean what I say. I love you; I have nothing else to say. Let us fly.

MME. DE SALLUS

Ah, you were altogether too cautious just now to become so brave all at once.

JACQUES DE RANDOL

Will you ever understand me? Listen to me. When I first realized that I adored you, I made a solemn vow concerning what might happen between you and me. The man who falls in love with a woman such as you, a woman married yet deserted; a slave in fact yet morally free, institutes between her and himself a bond which only she can break. The woman risks everything. Ay, it is just because she does this, because she gives everything — her heart, her body, her soul, her honor, her life, because she has foreseen all the miseries, all the dangers, all the misfortunes that can happen, because she dares to take so bold, and fearless a step, and because she is ready and determined to hazard everything — a husband who could kill her, and a world that would scorn her — it is for all this and for the heroism of her conjugal infidelity, that her lover, in taking her, ought to foresee all, to guard her against every ill that can possibly happen. I have nothing more to say. I spoke at first as a calm and foreseeing man who wished to protect you against everything — now I am simply and only the man who loves you. Order me as you please.

MME. DE SALLUS

That is all very prettily said; but is it true?

JACQUES DE RANDOL

I swear it!

MME. DE SALLUS

You wish to fly with me?

JACQUES DE RANDOL

Yes.

MME. DE SALLUS

From the bottom of your heart?

JACQUES DE RANDOL

From the bottom of my heart.

MME. DE SALLUS

To-day?

JACQUES DE RANDOL

Yes, and whenever you please.

MME. DE SALLUS

It is now a quarter to eight. My husband will be coming in directly, for we dine at eight. I shall be free at half past nine or ten o'clock.

JACQUES DE RANDOL

Where shall I wait for you?

MME. DE SALLUS

At the end of the street in a *coupé*. [*The bell rings.*] There he is, and for the last time, thank God!

Scene II.

(The same characters, and M. de Sallus.*)*

M. DE SALLUS [*enters.   To* Jacques de Randol, *who has risen to take his leave*]

Well, you are not going again, are you? Why, it seems that I need only come in to make you take your leave.

JACQUES DE RANDOL

No, no, my dear fellow; you don't make me go, but I must.

M. DE SALLUS

That is just what I say. You always go the very moment I come in. Of course, I understand that a husband is less attractive than a wife. But, at least, let me believe that *I* am not objectionable to you. [*Laughs.*]

JACQUES DE RANDOL

On the contrary, my dear fellow, you know I like you. And if you would acquire the habit of coming into your own house without ringing the bell, you would never find me taking my leave when you come.

M. DE SALLUS

How is that? Is it not natural to ring the door bell?

JACQUES DE RANDOL

Oh, yes; but a ring of the bell always makes me feel that I must go, and surely, coming into your own house, you can dispense with that habit.

M. DE SALLUS

I don't understand you.

JACQUES DE RANDOL

Why, it is very simple. When I visit people whom I like, such as Madame de Sallus and yourself, I do not expect to meet the Paris that flutters from house to house in the evening, gossiping and scandalizing. I have had my experience of gossip and tittle-tattle. It needs only one of these talkative dames or men to take away all the pleasure there is for me in visiting the lady on whom I happen to have called. Sometimes when I am anchored perforce upon my seat, I feel lost; I do not know how to get away. I have to take part in the whirlpool of foolish chatter. I know all the set questions and answers better than I do the catechism itself, and it bores me to have to remain until the very end and hear the very last opinion of some fool upon the comedy, or the book, or the divorce, or the marriage, or the death that is being discussed. Now, do you understand why I always get up and go at the sound of a bell?

M. DE SALLUS [*laughs*]

What you say is very true. Drawing-rooms now are not habitable from four o'clock to seven, and our

wives have no right to complain if we leave them to
go to the club.

MME. DE SALLUS [*sarcastically*]

Nevertheless, I do not see my way to receiving
ballet girls, or chorus girls, or actresses, or so-called
painters, poets, musicians, and others—in order to
keep you near me.

M. DE SALLUS

I do not ask so much as that. All I desire is a
few witty fellows, some charming women, and by no
means a crowd.

MME. DE SALLUS

You talk nonsense; you cannot pick and choose.

JACQUES DE RANDOL

No, truly, you cannot sift and strain the flow of
idiocy that you meet in the drawing-rooms of to-day.

M. DE SALLUS

Why?

MME. DE SALLUS

Simply because it is as it is—to-day.

M. DE SALLUS

What a pity! How I should love the intimacy of
a small and carefully selected circle of men and
women.

MME. DE SALLUS

You?

14   G. de M.—5

M. DE SALLUS

Yes, why not?

MME. DE SALLUS [*laughs*]

Ha, ha, ha! What a charming little intimate circle you would bring to me! Ha, ha, ha! The fascinating men, and the fashionable women that you would invite! My dear sir, it is I who would leave the house then.

M. DE SALLUS

My dear girl, I only asked for three or four women like yourself.

MME. DE SALLUS

Pray repeat that.

M. DE SALLUS

Three or four such women as you.

MME. DE SALLUS

If you need four, I can understand how you found your house lonesome.

M. DE SALLUS

You understand very well what I wish to say, and it is not necessary for me to explain myself. And you know that you need only be alone to please me better than I could possibly be pleased elsewhere.

MME. DE SALLUS

Really, I do not recognize you. I am afraid you must be ill—very ill. You are not going to die, are you?

M. DE SALLUS

Oh, chaff me as much as you like, you won't
worry me.

MME. DE SALLUS

And is this mood of yours going to last?

M. DE SALLUS

Forever.

MME. DE SALLUS

Men often change.

M. DE SALLUS [*turns to* Jacques de Randol]

My dear Randol, will you give us the pleasure of
your company at dinner to-night? You may help me
to turn aside the epigrams that my wife seems to
have barbed and ready for me.

JACQUES DE RANDOL

A thousand thanks, my dear Sallus! You are very,
very good, but unfortunately, I am not free.

M. DE SALLUS

But, my dear fellow, send your excuses.

JACQUES DE RANDOL

I cannot.

M. DE SALLUS

Are you dining in town?

JACQUES DE RANDOL

Yes, well—not altogether. I have an appointment at nine o'clock.

M. DE SALLUS

Is it very important?

JACQUES DE RANDOL

Very important.

M. DE SALLUS

With a lady?

JACQUES DE RANDOL

My dear fellow, what a question!

M. DE SALLUS

Oh, I am discreet! But that need not prevent you from dining with us.

JACQUES DE RANDOL

Thank you, my dear fellow, I cannot.

M. DE SALLUS

You know you can go away when you wish.

JACQUES DE RANDOL

But I am not in evening dress.

M. DE SALLUS

I can easily send for your things.

JACQUES DE RANDOL

No, truly, thank you; I cannot.

M. DE SALLUS [*to* Mme. de Sallus]

My dear girl, won't you keep Randol?

MME. DE SALLUS

Why ask me? You know that I have no influence over him.

M. DE SALLUS

You are charming enough to influence the world this evening, so why can't you make him stay?

MME. DE SALLUS

Good gracious! I cannot make my friends stay in order to please you, and keep them in your house against their wish. Bring *your* friends.

M. DE SALLUS

Well, I shall remain at home this evening in any case, and we shall then be *tête-à-tête*.

MME. DE SALLUS

Really?

M. DE SALLUS

Yes.

MME. DE SALLUS

You will be at home all the evening?

M. DE SALLUS

All the evening.

MME. DE SALLUS [*sarcastically*]

Good gracious! How you surprise me—and how you honor me!

M. DE SALLUS

No, it is a pleasure to be with you.

MME. DE SALLUS

What a charming mood you are in to-night!

M. DE SALLUS

Now ask Randol to remain.

MME. DE SALLUS

My dear sir, Monsieur de Randol will do as he pleases. He knows that I am always glad to see him. [*Rises, and after reflecting for a second.*] Will you dine with us, Monsieur de Randol? You know you can go directly after dinner.

JACQUES DE RANDOL

With the greatest pleasure, Madame.

MME. DE SALLUS

Excuse my absence for a minute. It is eight o'clock, and I must give some new directions for dinner.

[*Exit* Mme. de Sallus.

Scene III.

(M. de Sallus *and* M. Jacques de Randol.)

M. DE SALLUS

My dear fellow, you will do me the greatest service if you will pass the whole evening here.

JACQUES DE RANDOL

But I have told you that I cannot.

M. DE SALLUS

Is it altogether — absolutely — impossible?

JACQUES DE RANDOL

Absolutely.

M. DE SALLUS

I most earnestly ask you to remain.

JACQUES DE RANDOL

And why?

M. DE SALLUS

For the best of reasons — because — because I want to make peace with my wife.

JACQUES DE RANDOL

Peace? Is there a rupture between you?

M. DE SALLUS

Not a very great one, but you know what you have seen this evening.

JACQUES DE RANDOL

Is it your fault or hers?

M. DE SALLUS

Oh, mine, I suppose.

JACQUES DE RANDOL

The devil!

M. DE SALLUS

I have had annoyances outside, serious annoyances, and they have made me bad-tempered, so much so that I have been unpleasant and aggressive in my behavior toward her.

JACQUES DE RANDOL

But I don't see how a third party can contribute toward peace between you.

M. DE SALLUS

My dear fellow, you will enable me to make her understand in an indirect manner, while avoiding all indelicate and wounding explanations, that my ideas concerning life have altogether changed.

JACQUES DE RANDOL

Then you wish to be — to be — reconciled to her altogether?

M. DE SALLUS

Oh, no, no, no — on the contrary —

JACQUES DE RANDOL

Pardon me, I do not understand you.

M. DE SALLUS

Listen: I wish to establish and maintain a *status quo* of a pacific neutrality — a sort of Platonic peace. [*Laughs.*] But I am going into details that cannot interest you.

JACQUES DE RANDOL

Pardon me again. From the moment that you ask me to play a part in this very interesting affair, I must know exactly what part I am to play.

M. DE SALLUS

Why, just a conciliatory rôle.

JACQUES DE RANDOL

Then you wish to conclude a peace without restrictions for yourself?

M. DE SALLUS

Now you have it.

JACQUES DE RANDOL

That is to say, that, after the disappointments and annoyances of which you have just told me, and which I presume are ended, you wish to have peace at home and yet be free to enjoy any happiness that you may acquire outside.

M. DE SALLUS

Let me go farther. My dear fellow, the present situation between my wife and myself is very much strained, and I never care to find myself alone with her altogether, because my position is a false one.

JACQUES DE RANDOL

Oh, in that case, my dear fellow, I will remain.

M. DE SALLUS

All the evening?

JACQUES DE RANDOL

All the evening.

M. DE SALLUS

My dear De Randol, you are indeed a friend! I shall never forget it.

JACQUES DE RANDOL

Oh, never mind that. [*A short silence.*] Were you at the Opéra last night?

M. DE SALLUS

As usual.

JACQUES DE RANDOL

So it is a good performance?

M. DE SALLUS

Admirable.

JACQUES DE RANDOL

The Santelli scored a great success, didn't she?

M. DE SALLUS

Not only a success, but a veritable triumph. She was recalled six times.

JACQUES DE RANDOL

She *is* good, isn't she?

M. DE SALLUS

More than admirable. She never sang better. In
the first act she has a long recitative: "O God of
all believers, hear my prayer," which made the body
of the house rise to their feet. And in the third act,
after that phrase, "Bright heaven of beauty," I never
saw such enthusiasm.

JACQUES DE RANDOL

She was pleased?

M. DE SALLUS

Pleased? She was enchanted.

JACQUES DE RANDOL

You know her well, don't you?

M. DE SALLUS

Oh, yes, for some time back. I had supper with
her and some of her friends after the performance.

JACQUES DE RANDOL

Were there many of you?

M. DE SALLUS

No, about a dozen. You know she is rather
particular.

JACQUES DE RANDOL

It is pleasant to be intimate with her, is it not?

M. DE SALLUS

Exquisite! And then, you know, she is a woman
in a million. I do not know whether you agree with

me, but I find there are so few women that are
really women.

JACQUES DE RANDOL [*laughs*]

I have found that out.

M. DE SALLUS

Yes, and you have found out that there are women
who have a feminine air, but who are not women.

JACQUES DE RANDOL

Explain yourself.

M. DE SALLUS

Good gracious! Our society women, with very
rare exceptions, are simply pictures; they are pretty;
they are distinguished; but they charm you only in
their drawing-rooms. The part they play consists entirely in making men admire their dress, their dainty
ways, all of which are assumed.

JACQUES DE RANDOL

Men love them, nevertheless.

M. DE SALLUS

Oh, very rarely, my dear fellow.

JACQUES DE RANDOL

Pardon me!

M. DE SALLUS

Oh, yes, dreamers do. But men — real men —
men who are passionate, men who are positive, men

who are tender, do not love the society woman of
to-day, since she is incapable of love. My dear fellow, look around you. You see intrigues — everyone
sees them; but can you lay your finger upon a single
real love affair — a love that is disinterested, such a
love as there used to be — inspired by a single woman
of our acquaintance? Don't I speak the truth? It
flatters a man to have a mistress — it flatters him, it
amuses him, and then it tires him. But turn to the
other picture and look at the woman of the stage.
There is not one who has not at least five or six
love affairs on the carpet; idiotic follies, causing
bankruptcy, scandal, and suicides. Men love them;
yes, they love these women because these women
know how to inspire love, and because they are loving women. Yes, indeed, *they* know how to conquer men; they understand the seduction of a smile;
they know how to attract, seize, and wrap us up in
their hearts, how to enslave us with a look, and they
need not be beautiful at that. They have a conquer-
ing power that we never find in our wives.

JACQUES DE RANDOL

And the Santelli is a seductress of this kind?

M. DE SALLUS

She is first among the first! Ah, the cunning
little coquette! *She* knows how to make men run
after her.

JACQUES DE RANDOL

Does she do only that?

M. DE SALLUS

A woman of that sort does not give herself the trouble of making men run after her unless she has some further object in view.

JACQUES DE RANDOL

The devil! You make me believe you attend two first nights in the same evening.

M. DE SALLUS

My dear boy, don't imagine such a thing.

JACQUES DE RANDOL

Great heavens! you have such a satisfied and triumphant air — an air so desirous of calm at home. If I am deceived I am sorry — for your sake.

M. DE SALLUS

Well, we will assume that you are deceived and —

SCENE IV.

(*The same, and* Mme. de Sallus.)

M. DE SALLUS [*gaily*]

Well, my dear, Jacques remains. He has consented for my sake.

MME. DE SALLUS

I congratulate you. And how did you achieve that miracle?

M. DE SALLUS

Oh, easily enough, in the course of conversation.

MME. DE SALLUS

And of what have you been talking?

JACQUES DE RANDOL

Of the happiness that comes to a man who remains quietly at home.

MME. DE SALLUS

That sort of happiness has but little attraction for me. I like the excitement of travel.

JACQUES DE RANDOL

There is a time for everything; and travel is very often inopportune and very inconvenient.

MME. DE SALLUS

But how about that important appointment of yours at nine o'clock? Have you given it up altogether, Monsieur de Randol?

JACQUES DE RANDOL

I have, Madame.

MME. DE SALLUS

You are very changeable.

JACQUES DE RANDOL

No, no, I am simply adapting myself to circumstances.

M. DE SALLUS

Will you pardon me if I write a note? [*Sits at desk at the other end of the drawing-room.*]

MME. DE SALLUS [*to* Jacques de Randol]

What has happened?

JACQUES DE RANDOL

Oh, nothing; everything is all right.

MME. DE SALLUS

When do we go?

JACQUES DE RANDOL

Not at all.

MME. DE SALLUS

Are you mad? Why?

JACQUES DE RANDOL

Please don't ask me now about it.

MME. DE SALLUS

I am sure that he is laying a trap for us.

JACQUES DE RANDOL

Not at all. He is very quiet, very contented, and has absolutely no suspicion.

MME. DE SALLUS

Then what does it all mean?

JACQUES DE RANDOL

Now, be calm. He is happy, I tell you.

MME. DE SALLUS

That is not true.

JACQUES DE RANDOL

I tell you it is. He has made me the confidant of all his happiness.

MME. DE SALLUS

It is just a trick; he wishes to watch us.

JACQUES DE RANDOL

Oh, no; he is confiding and conciliatory. The only fear he has is of you.

MME. DE SALLUS

Of me ?

JACQUES DE RANDOL

Yes; in the same way that you are, all the time, afraid of him.

MME. DE SALLUS

Great heavens! You have lost your head. You are talking at random.

JACQUES DE RANDOL

Listen — I am sure that he intends to go out this evening.

MME. DE SALLUS

Well, in that case, let us go out too.

JACQUES DE RANDOL

No, no, — I tell you there is nothing more for us to fear.

14 G. de M.—6

MME. DE SALLUS

What nonsense! You will end by maddening me with your blindness.

M. DE SALLUS [*from the other end of the drawing-room*]

My dear, I have some good news for you. I have been able to get another night at the Opera for you every week.

MME. DE SALLUS

Really, it is very good of you to afford me the opportunity of applauding Madame Santelli so often.

M. DE SALLUS [*from the same place*]

Well, she is very clever.

JACQUES DE RANDOL

And everybody says she is charming.

MME. DE SALLUS [*irritably*]

Yes; it is only such women who please men.

JACQUES DE RANDOL

You are unjust.

MME. DE SALLUS

Oh, my dear Randol; it is only for such women that men commit follies, and [*sarcastically*], understand me, the measure of a man's folly is often the measure of his love.

M. DE SALLUS [*from the same place*]

Oh, no, my dear girl,—men do not marry them, and marriage is the only real folly that a man can commit with a woman.

MME. DE SALLUS

A beautiful idea, truly, when a woman has to endure all man's caprices.

JACQUES DE RANDOL

Oh, no, not having anything to lose, they have nothing to risk.

MME. DE SALLUS

Ah, men are sad creatures! They marry a young girl because she is demure and self-contained, and they leave her on the morrow to dangle after a girl who is not young and who certainly is not demure, her chief attraction being that all the rich and well-known men about town have at one time been in her favor. The more danglers she has after her, the more she is esteemed, the more she is sought after, and the more she is respected; that is to say, with that kind of Parisian respect which accrues to a woman in the degree of her notoriety—a notoriety due either to the scandal she creates, or the scandal men create about her. Ah, yes, you men are so nice in these things!

M. DE SALLUS [*laughs gently*]

Take care! One would think you were jealous.

MME. DE SALLUS

I? Jealous? For whom do you take me? [*The butler announces.*] Madame is served. [*Hands a letter to* M. de Sallus.]

MME. DE SALLUS [*to* Jacques de Randol]

Your arm, M. Jacques de Randol.

JACQUES DE RANDOL [*in a low tone*]

How I love you!

MME. DE SALLUS [*indifferently*]

Just a little, I suppose.

JACQUES DE RANDOL

Ah, no; with all my soul!

M. DE SALLUS [*after reading his letter*]

Come along, then, let us go to dinner. I have to go out this evening.

Curtain.

MUSOTTE

OR

A CRITICAL SITUATION

A COMEDY IN THREE ACTS

BY

GUY DE MAUPASSANT

AND

JACQUES NORMAND

PRODUCED AT THE COMÉDIE FRANÇAISE IN 1891

VOL. XIV

M. WALTER DUNNE, PUBLISHER
NEW YORK AND LONDON

MUSOTTE

DRAMATIS PERSONÆ

JEAN MARTINEL
> Nephew of M. Martinel, a painter; not yet thirty years of age, but already well known and the recipient of various honors.

LÉON DE PETITPRÉ
> Brother to Gilberte Martinel, a young lawyer about thirty years of age.

M. MARTINEL
> An old gunmaker of Havre, aged fifty-five.

M. DE PETITPRÉ
> An old magistrate, officer of the Legion of Honor. Aged sixty.

DR. PELLERIN
> A fashionable physician of about thirty-five.

MME. DE RONCHARD
> Sister to M. de Petitpré, about fifty-five years of age.

HENRIETTE LÉVÊQUE
> Nicknamed Musotte; a little model, formerly Jean Martinel's mistress. Twenty-two years of age.

MME. FLACHE
> A midwife. Formerly a ballet-dancer at the Opera. About thirty-five years of age.

GILBERTE MARTINEL
> Daughter of M. and Mme. de Petitpré, married in the morning to Jean Martinel. About twenty years old.

LISE BABIN
> A nurse, about twenty-six.

SERVANTS

Time: Paris of to-day. The first and third acts take place in M. de Petitpré's *drawing-room.*
The second act takes place in Musotte's *bedchamber.*

ACT I.

SCENE I.

(*A richly yet classically furnished drawing-room in* M. de Petitpré's *house. A table,* C.; *sofas,* R.; *chairs and armchairs,* L. *Wide doors,* C., *opening upon a terrace or gallery. Doors* R. *and* L. *of* C. *Lighted lamps.*)

Enter from R. M. de Petitpré, Monsieur Martinel, Madame de Ronchard, Léon de Petitpré, Jean *and* Gilberte. Gilberte *is in her bridal attire, but without wreath and veil.*

MME. DE RONCHARD [*after bowing to* M. Martinel, *whose arm she relinquishes, seats herself* R.]

GILBERTE, Gilberte!

      GILBERTE [*leaves Jean's arm*]

What is it, Auntie?

      MME. DE RONCHARD

The coffee, my dear child.

      GILBERTE [*goes to the table*]

I will give you some, Auntie.

      MME. DE RONCHARD

Don't soil your gown.

(3)

LÉON [*comes up*]

No, no, not to-day shall my sister serve coffee. The day of her marriage! No, indeed, I will take care of that. [*To* Mme. de Ronchard.] You know that I am a lawyer, my dear Aunt, and therefore can do everything.

MME. DE RONCHARD

Oh, I know your abilities, Léon, and I appreciate them —

LÉON [*smiles, and gives his Aunt a cup of coffee*]

You are too good.

MME. DE RONCHARD [*taking cup, dryly*]

For what they are worth.

LÉON [*aside, turns to the table*]

There she goes again — another little slap at me! That is never wanting. [*offers a cup to* Martinel.] You will take a small cup, won't you, M. Martinel, and a nip of old brandy with it? I know your tastes. We will take good care of you.

MARTINEL

Thank you, Léon.

LÉON [*to* Petitpré]

Will you have a cup, father?

PETITPRÉ

I will, my son.

LÉON [*to the newly married couple, seated* L. *and talking aside*]

And you, you bridal pair there? [*The couple, absorbed in each other, do not answer.*] Oh, I suppose we must not bother you. [*He sets cup down on the table*].

PETITPRÉ [*to* Martinel]

You don't smoke, I believe?

MARTINEL

Never, thank you.

MME. DE RONCHARD

You astonish me! My brother and Léon would not miss smoking each day for anything in the world. But what an abomination a cigar is!

PETITPRÉ

A delicious abomination, Clarisse.

LÉON [*turns to* Mme. de Ronchard]

Almost all abominations are delicious, Auntie; in fact many of them, to my personal knowledge, are exquisite

MME. DE RONCHARD

You naughty fellow!

PETITPRÉ [*takes* Léon's *arm*]

Come and smoke in the billiard-room, since your Aunt objects to it here.

LÉON [*to* Petitpré]

The day when she will love anything except her spaniels —

PETITPRÉ

Hold your tongue and come along.   [*Exit* C.]

MARTINEL [*to* Mme. de Ronchard]

This is the sort of marriage that I like — a marriage that, in this Paris of yours, you don't have very often. After the wedding breakfast, which takes place directly after you come from the church, all the guests go home, even the maids of honor and the ushers. The married couple remain at home and dine with their parents or relatives. In the evening they play billiards or cards, just as on an ordinary night; the newly married couple entertain each other. [Gilberte *and* Jean *rise, and hand in hand slowly retire* C.] Then, before midnight, good night!

MME. DE RONCHARD [*aside*]

Which is altogether very *bourgeois!*

MARTINEL [*sits* R. *upon the sofa beside* Mme. de Ronchard]

As to newly married couples — instead of going on that absurd and traditional thing you call a honeymoon, it is far better for them to go at once to the apartment or house prepared for them. I dare say you will think my plan lacking in fashion and display, but I cannot help that. For myself, I must say that I like absence of all ostentation.

MME. DE RONCHARD

Your plan is not according to the customs of polite society, Monsieur.

MARTINEL

Polite society, indeed! Why, there are thirty-six different kinds of polite society. For instance, take Havre.

MME. DE RONCHARD [*interrupts*]

I know only ours. [*Corrects herseif.*] That is, I mean to say, mine, which is the correct one.

MARTINEL

Oh, naturally, naturally! Nevertheless, simple as it may be, this marriage is an acknowledged fact, and I hope that you have taken into your good books my dear nephew, who, until now —

MME. DE RONCHARD

I can hardly help doing so since he is my brother's son-in-law, and my niece's husband.

MARTINEL

Well, that is not the only thing, is it? I am very happy that the affair is over — although my life has been spent in the midst of difficulties.

MME. DE RONCHARD

What! Your life?

MARTINEL

I mean commercial difficulties, not matrimonial.

14   G. de M.—7

MME. DE RONCHARD

What commercial difficulties can you have — you, a Crœsus who has just given five hundred thousand francs in dowry to his nephew. [*With a sigh.*] Five hundred thousand francs! Just what my late husband squandered.

MARTINEL

Oh! Yes, I know that, Madame de Ronchard.

MME. DE RONCHARD [*sighs again*]

I was ruined and deserted after just one year of married life, Monsieur — one year. I just had time to realize how happy I could be, for the scoundrel, the wretch, knew how to make me love him.

MARTINEL

Then he was a scoundrel?

MME. DE RONCHARD

Oh! Monsieur, he was a man of fashion.

MARTINEL

Well, that did not prevent him from —

MME. DE RONCHARD

Oh, don't let us talk any more about my misfortunes. It would be too long and too sad, and everybody else is so happy here just now.

MARTINEL

And I am happier than anybody else, I assure
you. My nephew is such a good fellow. I love him
as I would a son. Now, as for myself, I made my
fortune in trade —

MME. DE RONCHARD [*aside*]

That is very evident.

MARTINEL [*resumes*]

In the sea-going trade. But my nephew will gain
fame for our name by his renown as an artist; the
only difference between us is that he makes his fortune with his brushes, and I have made mine with
ships. Art, to-day, Madame, may be as important as
trade, but it is less profitable. Take my nephew.
Although he has made a very early success, it is I
who have enabled him to. When my poor brother
died, his wife following him almost immediately, I
found myself, while quite a young man, left alone
with this baby. Well, I made him learn everything
that I could. He studied chemistry, music, and lit-
erature, but he had a leaning toward art more than
to the other things. I assure you that I encouraged
him in it, and you see how he has succeeded. He is
only just thirty, is well known, and has just been
decorated.

MME. DE RONCHARD [*dryly*]

Thirty years old, and only just decorated; that is
slow for an artist.

MARTINEL

Pshaw! He will make up for lost time. [*Rises*]
But I am afraid I am getting boastful. You must
pardon me, I am a plain man, and just now a little
exhilarated by dining. It is all Petitpré's fault. His
Burgundy is excellent. It is a wine that you may
say is a friend to wisdom. And we are accustomed
to drink a good deal at Havre. [*Takes up his glass
of brandy and finishes it.*]

MME. DE RONCHARD [*aside*]

Surely that is enough about Havre.

MARTINEL [*turns to* Mme. de Ronchard]

Well, there is a treaty between us — a treaty which
will last — which no foolishness can break, such as
that which has failed to break this marriage.

MME. DE RONCHARD [*rises and crosses* L.]

Foolishness! You speak very lightly about it.
But now that the marriage is a thing accomplished,
it is all right. I had destined my niece for another
sphere than a painter's world. However, when you
can't get a thrush, eat a blackbird, as the proverb
says.

MARTINEL

But a white blackbird, Madame, for your niece is
a pearl. Let me tell you, the happiness of these
children will be the happiness of my declining years.

MME. DE RONCHARD

I wish that it may be, Monsieur, without daring to hope for it.

MARTINEL

Never mind. There are two things on which I am an expert—the merits of women and of wine.

MME. DE RONCHARD [*aside*]

Especially upon the latter.

MARTINEL

They are the only two things worth knowing in life.

SCENE II.

(*The same characters and* Petitpré *who enters* C. *with* Léon.)

PETITPRÉ

Now that this red-letter day has gone by as any other day goes, will you play a game of billiards with me, Monsieur Martinel?

MARTINEL

Most certainly, I am very fond of billiards.

LÉON [*comes down stage*]

You are like my father. It seems to me that when anyone begins to like billiards at all, they become infatuated with the game; and you two people are two of a kind.

MARTINEL

My son, when a man grows old, and has no family, he has to take refuge in such pleasures as these. If you take bait-fishing as your diversion in the morning and billiards for the afternoon and evening, you have two kinds of amusement that are both worthy and attractive.

LÉON

Oh, ho! Bait-fishing, indeed! That means to say, getting up early and sitting with your feet in the water through wind and rain in the hope of catching, perhaps each quarter of an hour, a fish about the size of a match. And you call that an attractive pastime?

MARTINEL

I do, without a doubt. But do you believe that there is a single lover in the world capable of doing as much for his mistress throughout ten, twelve, or fifteen years of life? If you asked my opinion, I think he would give it up at the end of a fortnight.

MME. DE RONCHARD

Of a truth, he would.

LÉON [interrupts]

Pardon me, I should give it up at the end of a week.

MARTINEL

You speak sensibly.

PETITPRÉ

Come along, my dear fellow.

MARTINEL

Shall we play fifty up?

PETITPRÉ

Fifty up will do.

MARTINEL [*turns to* Mme. de Ronchard]

We shall see you again shortly, Madame.

MME. DE RONCHARD

Well, I have had enough of Havre for the present.

[*Exit* Martinel *and* Petitpré C.

SCENE III.

(Léon *and* Mme. de Ronchard.)

LÉON

Martinel is a good fellow. Not a man of culture, but bright as sunshine and straight as a rule.

MME. DE RONCHARD [*seated* L.]

He is lacking in distinction of manner.

LÉON [*inadvertently*]

How about yourself, Aunt?

MME. DE RONCHARD

What do you mean?

LÉON [*corrects himself and approaches* Mme. de Ronchard]

I said, how about yourself? You know what I mean — you have such an intimate knowledge of the world that you are a better judge of human nature than anyone I know.

MME. DE RONCHARD

Indeed, I am. You were too small a boy to recollect it, but nevertheless, I went a great deal into society before my husband spent all my money, and let me tell you that I was a great success. For instance, at a grand ball given by the Turkish ambassador, at which I was dressed as Salammbô —

LÉON [*interrupts*]
What, you, the Carthaginian princess?

MME. DE RONCHARD

Certainly. Why not? Let me tell you that I was greatly admired, for my appearance was exquisite. My dear, that was in eighteen hundred and sixty —

LÉON [*sits near* Mme. de Ronchard]
Oh, no dates! for goodness sake, no dates!

MME. DE RONCHARD

It is not necessary to be sarcastic.

LÉON

What! I, sarcastic? God forbid! It is simply this: in view of the fact that you did not wish this marriage to take place, and that I did, and that the marriage has taken place, I feel very happy. Do you understand me? It is a triumph for me, and I must confess that I feel very triumphant this evening. To-morrow, however, vanish the triumpher, and there will remain only your affectionate little nephew. Come, smile, Auntie. At heart you are not as ill-natured as you pretend to be, and that is proved by the generosity of soul you have evinced in founding at Neuilly, despite your modest means, a hospital for —lost dogs!

MME. DE RONCHARD

What else could I do. When a woman is alone and has no children — and I was married such a short time — do you know what I am, after all? Simply an old maid, and like all old maids —

LÉON [*finishes the sentence for her*]

You love toy dogs.

MME. DE RONCHARD

As much as I hate men.

LÉON

You mean to say one man. Well, I could hardly blame you for hating him.

MME. DE RONCHARD

And you know for what kind of girl he abandoned and ruined me. You never saw her, did you?

LÉON

Pardon me, I did see her once in the Champs-Elysées. I was walking with you and my father. A

gentleman and lady came toward us; you became excited, quickened your steps, and clutched nervously
at my father's arm, and I heard you say in a low
voice, "Don't look at them; it is she!"

MME. DE RONCHARD

And what were you doing?

LÉON

I?—I was looking at him.

MME. DE RONCHARD [*rises*]

And you thought her horrible, didn't you?

LÉON

I really don't know.   You know I was only eleven
years old.

MME. DE RONCHARD [*crosses* R.]

You are insufferable!   Go away, or I shall strike
you.

LÉON [*soothingly, and rising*]

There, there, Aunt, I won't do it again.   I will be
good, I promise you, if you will forgive me.

MME. DE RONCHARD [*rises, as if to go out* C.]

I will not!

LÉON

Please do!

his studio for hours at a time, and everybody knows
what goes on in those studios.

LÉON

You have been accustomed to go there, my dear
Aunt?

MME. DE RONCHARD [*dreamily*]

Oh, yes. [*Corrects herself.*] I mean to say, once
I went to Horace Vernet's studio.

LÉON

The painter of battle scenes!

MME. DE RONCHARD

Well, what I say of Jean, I say of all artists — that
they ought not to be allowed to marry into a family
of lawyers and magistrates, such as ours. Such do-
ings always bring trouble. I ask you as a man, is it
possible to be a good husband under such conditions
— among a crowd of women continually around you,
who do nothing but unrobe and re-dress themselves,
whether they be clients or models (*pointedly*), especially models? [Mme. de Ronchard *rises and* Léon *is
silent.*] I said *models*, Léon.

LÉON

I understand you, Aunt. You make a very pointed
and delicate allusion to Jean's past. Well, what of
it? If he did have one of his models for a mistress,
he loved her, and loved her sincerely for three
years —

MME. DE RONCHARD

You mean to tell me a man can love such women?

LÉON

Every woman can be loved, my dear Aunt; and this woman certainly deserved to be loved more than most women.

MME. DE RONCHARD

A great thing, truly, for a model to be pretty! That is the essential thing, I should think.

LÉON

Whether it be essential or not, it is nevertheless very nice to be pretty. But this girl was better than pretty, for she had a nature which was exceptionally tender, good, and sincere.

MME. DE RONCHARD

Well, then, why did he leave her?

LÉON

What! Can you ask me such a question? — you, who know so much about the world and the world's opinions? [*Folds his arms.*] Would you advocate free love?

MME. DE RONCHARD [*indignantly*]

You know I would not.

LÉON [*seriously*]

Listen. The truth is, that it happened to Jean as it has happened to many others besides him — that is to say, there was a pretty little nineteen-year-old girl whom he met, whom he loved, and with whom he established an intimacy little by little — an intimacy which lasted one, two, three years — the usual duration of that sort of thing. Then, as usually happens, there came a rupture — a rupture which is sometimes violent, sometimes gentle, but which is never altogether good-natured. Then also, as usual in such cases, each went a separate way — the eternal ending, which is always prosaic, because it is true to life. But the one thing that distinguishes Jean's *liaison* from the usual affair is the truly admirable character of the girl in the case.

MME. DE RONCHARD

Oh, admirable character! Mademoiselle — tell me, what is the name of this young lady? If you mentioned it I have forgotten it. Mademoiselle Mus — Mus —

LÉON

Musotte, Auntie; little Musotte.

MME. DE RONCHARD

Musette! Pshaw, that's a very common name. It reminds me of the Latin quarter and of Bohemian life. [*With disgust.*] Musette!

LÉON

No, no; not Musette. Musotte, with an O instead of an E. She is named Musotte because of her pretty little nose; can't you understand? Musotte, the name explains itself.

MME. DE RONCHARD [*with contempt*]

Oh, yes; a *fin-de-siècle* Musotte, which is still worse. Musotte is not a name.

LÉON

My dear Aunt, it is only a nickname. The nickname of a model. Her true name is Henriette Lévêque.

MME. DE RONCHARD [*puzzled*]

Lévêque?

LÉON

Yes, Lévêque. What does this questioning mean? It is just as I told you, or else I know nothing about it. Now, Henriette Lévêque, or Musotte, if you prefer that term, has not only been faithful to Jean during the course of her love affair with him; has not only been devoted and adoring, and full of a tenderness which was ever watchful, but at the very hour of her rupture with him, she gave proof of her greatness of soul. She accepted everything without reproach, without recrimination; the poor little girl understood everything — understood that all was finished and finished forever. With the intuition of a woman, she felt that Jean's love for my sister was real and deep, she bowed her head to circumstances and she departed, accepting, without a murmur, the loneliness that Jean's action brought upon her. She carried her fidelity to the end, for she would have slain herself sooner than become [*hesitating out of respect for* Mme. de Ronchard] a courtesan. And this I *know*.

MME. DE RONCHARD

And has Jean never seen her since?

LÉON

Not once; and that is more than eight months ago. He wished for news of her, and he gave me the task of getting it. I never found her and I have never been able to gain any knowledge of her, so cunningly did she arrange this flight of hers — this flight which was so noble and so self-sacrificing. [*Changing his tone.*] But I don't know why I repeat all this. You know it just as well as I do, for I have told it to you a dozen times.

MME. DE RONCHARD

It is just as incredible at the twentieth time as at the first.

LÉON

It is nevertheless the truth.

MME. DE RONCHARD [*sarcastically*]

Well, if it is really the truth, you were terribly wrong in helping Jean to break his connection with such an admirable woman.

LÉON

Oh, no, Aunt, I only did my duty. You have even called me hairbrained, and perhaps you were right; but you know that I can be very serious when I wish. If this three-year-old *liaison* had lasted until now, Jean would have been ruined.

14 G. de M.—8

MME. DE RONCHARD

Well, how could we help that?

LÉON

Well, these things are frightful — these entangle-
ments — I can't help using the word. It was my
duty as a friend — and I wish to impress it upon
you — to rescue Jean; and as a brother, it was my
duty to marry my sister to such a man as he. The
future will tell you whether I was right or not.
[*Coaxingly*.] And then, my dear Aunt, when later
you have a little nephew or a little niece to take
care of, to dandle in your arms, you will banish all
these little spaniels that you are taking care of at
Neuilly.

MME. DE RONCHARD

The poor little darlings! I, abandon them! Don't
you know that I love them as a mother loves her
children?

LÉON

Oh, yes; you can become an aunt to them, then,
because you will have to become a mother to your
little nephew.

MME. DE RONCHARD

Oh, hold your tongue; you irritate me.

(Jean *appears with* Gilberte *for a moment at* C.)

JEAN [*to servant entering* R.]

Joseph, have you forgotten nothing, especially the
flowers?

SERVANT

Monsieur and Madame may rest assured that everything has been done. [*Exit servant* L.

LÉON [*to* Mme. de Ronchard]

Look at them; aren't they a bonny couple?

SCENE IV.

(*The same with* Jean *and* Gilberte.)

JEAN [*approaches* Mme. de Ronchard *and speaks to her*]

Do you know of whom we were talking just now? We were talking of you.

LÉON [*aside*]

Ahem! ahem!

JEAN

Yes; I was just saying that I had not made you a present on the occasion of my nuptials, because the choosing of it demanded a great deal of reflection.

MME. DE RONCHARD [*dryly*]

But Gilberte made me a very pretty one for you both, Monsieur.

JEAN

But that is not enough. I have been looking for something which I thought would be particularly ac-

ceptable to you; and do you know what I found?
It is a very small thing, but I ask you, Madame, to
be so good as to accept this little pocketbook, which
holds some bank-notes, for the benefit of your dear
little deserted pets. You can add to your home for
these little pets some additional kennels on the sole
condition that you will allow me from time to time
to come and pet your little pensioners, and on the
additional condition that you will not pick out the
most vicious among them to greet me.

MME. DE RONCHARD [*greatly impressed*]

With all my heart, I thank you. How good of
you to think of my poor little orphans!

LÉON [*whispers to* Jean]

You diplomat, you!

JEAN

There is nothing extraordinary about it, Madame.
I am very fond of dumb animals. They are really
the foster-brothers of man, sacrificed for them, slaves
to them, and in many cases their food. They are the
true martyrs of the world.

MME. DE RONCHARD

What you say is very true, Monsieur, and I have
often thought of it in that way. For instance, take
those poor horses, scourged and beaten by coachmen
in the streets.

LÉON [*with sarcastic emphasis*]

And the pheasants, Auntie, and the partridges and
the blackcock falling on all sides under a hail of

lead, flying panic-stricken before the horrible massacre of the guns.

MME. DE RONCHARD

Oh, don't talk like that, it makes me shudder; it is horrible!

JEAN [*turns to* Gilberte]

Horrible, indeed!

LÉON [*after a pause, in light tone*]

Perhaps so, but they are good eating.

MME. DE RONCHARD

You are pitiless.

LÉON [*aside to his aunt*]

Pitiless, perhaps, toward animals, but not pitiless, like you, toward people.

MME. DE RONCHARD [*in the same tone*]

What do you mean by that?

LÉON [*in the same tone pointing to* Jean *and* Gilberte, *who are seated on a sofa* R.]

Do you think that your presence here can be acceptable to those two lovers? [*Takes her arm.*] My father has certainly finished smoking; come into the billiard-room for a little while.

MME. DE RONCHARD

And what are you going to do?

LÉON

I am going down into my study on the ground floor, and I shall come up here after a little while.

MME. DE RONCHARD [*sarcastically*]

Your study, indeed — your studio — you mean, you rascal, where your clients are — models —

LÉON [*with mock modesty*]

Oh, Auntie. My clients, at least, don't unrobe — alas! [*Exit* Léon R., *giving a mock benediction to the lovers.*] Children, receive my benediction!

[*Exit* Madame de Ronchard C.

SCENE V.

(Jean *and* Gilberte *seated on the sofa at right.*)

JEAN

At last, you are my wife, Mademoiselle.

GILBERTE

Mademoiselle?

JEAN

Forgive me. I hardly know how to address you.

GILBERTE

Call me Gilberte. There is nothing shocking about that, is there?

JEAN

Gilberte, at last, at last, at last, you are my wife!

GILBERTE

And truly, not without a good deal of trouble.

JEAN

And what a dainty, energetic little creature you are! How you fought with your father, and with your aunt, for it is only through you, and thanks to you, that we are married, for which I thank you with all my heart—the heart which belongs to you.

GILBERTE

But it is only because I trusted you, and that is all.

JEAN

And have you only trust for me?

GILBERTE

Stupid boy! You know that you pleased me. If you had only pleased me, my confidence in you would have been useless. One must love first. Without that, Monsieur, nothing can come.

JEAN

Call me Jean, just as I have called you Gilberte.

GILBERTE [*hesitates*]

But that is not altogether the same thing. It seems to me—that—that—I cannot do it. [*Rises and crosses* L.]

JEAN [*rises*]

But I love you. I am no trifler, believe me; I love you. I am the man who loves you because he has found in you qualities that are inestimable. You are one of those perfect creatures who have as much brains as sentiment; and the sentimentality that permeates you is not the sickly sentimentality of ordinary women. It is that gloriously beautiful faculty of tenderness which characterizes great souls, and which one never meets elsewhere in the world. And then, you are so beautiful, so graceful, with a grace that is all your own, and I, who am a painter, you know how I adore the beautiful. Then, above everything, you drew me to you, but not only that, you wiped out the traces of the world from my mind and eyes.

GILBERTE

I like to hear you say that. But, don't talk any more just now in that way, because it embarrasses me. However, I know, for I try to foresee everything, that to enjoy these things I must listen to them to-day, for your words breathe the passion of a lover. Perhaps in the future your words will be as sweet, for they could not help being so when a man speaks as you spoke and loves as you appear to love, but at the same time, they will be different.

JEAN

Oh!

GILBERTE [sits on stool near the table]

Tell me it over again.

JEAN

What drew me to you was the mysterious harmony between your natural form and the soul within it. Do you recollect my first visit to this house?

AFTER AN ORIGINAL DRAWING BY J. C. FIREMAN.

"Tell me it over again."

GILBERTE

Oh, yes, very well. My brother brought you to
dinner, and I believe that you did not wish to
come.

JEAN [*laughs*]

If that were true, it was very indiscreet of your
brother to tell you. And he told you that? I am annoyed that he did so, and I confess I did hesitate
somewhat, for you know I was an artist accustomed
to the society of artists, which is lively, witty, and
sometimes rather free, and I felt somewhat disturbed
at the idea of entering a house so serious as yours —
a house peopled by dignified lawyers and young
ladies. But I was so fond of your brother, I found
him so full of novelty, so gay, so wittily sarcastic
and discerning, under his assumed levity, that not
only did I go everywhere with him, but I followed
him to the extent of meeting you. And I never cease
to thank him for it. Do you remember when I entered the drawing-room where you and your family
were sitting, you were arranging in a china vase
some flowers that had just been sent to you?

GILBERTE

I do.

JEAN

Your father spoke to me of my Uncle Martinel,
whom he had formerly known. This at once formed
a link between us, for all the time that I was talking
to him I was watching you arrange your flowers.

GILBERTE [*smiles*]

You looked far too long and too steadfastly for a first introduction.

JEAN

I was looking at you as an artist looks, and was admiring you, for I found your figure, your movements, and your entire self attractive. And then for the last six months I have often come to this house, to which your brother invited me and whither your presence attracted me, and finally I felt your sway as a lover feels the sway of the one he adores. There was an inexplicable, unseen attraction calling me to you. [*Sits beside her R. of table.*] Then a dim idea entered my brain,—an idea that one day you might become my wife. It gained possession of my soul, and I immediately took steps to renew the friendship between your father and my uncle. The two men again became friends. Did you never divine my maneuvers?

GILBERTE

Divine your maneuvers? No, I suspected a little at times, but I was so astounded that a man like you —in the full flush of success, so well known, so sought after—should concern himself with such a little, unimportant girl as I, that, really, I could place no faith in the sincerity of your attention.

JEAN

Nevertheless, we quickly knew how to understand each other, did we not?

GILBERTE

Your character pleased me. I felt that you were loyal, and then you entertained me greatly, for you brought into our house that artistic air which gave my fancies life. I ought to tell you that my brother had already warned me that I should like you. You know that Léon loves you.

JEAN

I know it, and I think it was in *his* brain that the first idea of our marriage had birth. [*After a short silence.*] You remember our return from Saint-Germain after we had dined in the Henri IV. Pavilion?

GILBERTE

I remember it well.

JEAN

My uncle and your aunt were in the front of the landau, and you and I on the rear seat, and in another carriage were your father and Léon. What a glorious spring night! But how coldly you treated me!

GILBERTE

I was so embarrassed!

JEAN

You ought to recall that I put to you that day a question which I had already asked you, because you cannot deny that I had paid you very tender attention and that you had captured my heart.

GILBERTE

True. Nevertheless it surprised and upset me. Oh, how often have I remembered it since! But I have never been able to recall the very words you used. Do you remember them?

JEAN

No; they came from my lips, issuing from the bottom of my heart like a prayer for mercy. I only know that I told you that I should never re-enter your house if you did not give me some little hope that there should be a day when you would know me better. You pondered a long time before you answered me, but you spoke in such a low tone that I was anxious to make you repeat it.

GILBERTE [takes up his sentence and speaks as if in a dream]

I said that it would pain me greatly if I should see you no more.

JEAN

Yes, that is what you said.

GILBERTE

You have forgotten nothing!

JEAN

Could anyone forget that? [With deep emotion.] Do you know what I think? As we look at each other and examine our hearts, our souls, our mutual understanding, our love, I verily believe that we have set out on the true road to happiness. [Kisses her. For a moment they are silent.]

GILBERTE [*rises*]

But I must leave you. [*Goes toward door* L.] I must prepare for our journey. Meanwhile, go and find my father.

JEAN [*follows her*]

Yes, but tell me before you go that you love me.

GILBERTE

Yes — I love you.

JEAN [*kisses her forehead*]

My only one.

[*Exit* Gilberte L., *a second after. Enter* M. Martinel C. *with a very agitated air, and a letter in his hand.*]

MARTINEL [*perceives* Jean, *quickly slips the letter into his pocket; then, recollecting himself*]

Have you seen Léon?

JEAN

No, are you looking for him?

MARTINEL

No, no, I have just a word to say to him concerning an engagement of small importance.

JEAN [*perceives* Léon]

Wait a moment.   Here he comes.

[*Enter* Léon R. *Exit* Jean. C.

Scene VI.

(Martinel *and* Léon.)

MARTINEL [*goes quickly up to* Léon]

I must have five minutes with you. Something terrible has happened. Never in the course of my life have I been placed in so awkward and so embarrassing a situation.

LÉON

Quick! What is it?

MARTINEL

I had just finished my game at billiards when a servant brought me a letter addressed to M. Martinel, without any Christian name by which to identify it, but with these words on the letter "Exceedingly urgent." I thought it was addressed to me, so I tore open the envelope, and I read words intended for Jean — words which have well-nigh taken away my reason. I came to find you in order to ask advice, for this is a thing which must be decided upon the moment.

LÉON

Tell me, what is it?

MARTINEL

I am responsible for my own actions, M. Léon, and I would ask advice of no one if the matter concerned myself only, but unfortunately it concerns Jean; therefore, I hesitate — the matter is so grave, and then the secret is not mine—I came upon it accidentally.

LÉON

Tell me quickly, and do not doubt my faith.

MARTINEL

I do not doubt your faith. Here is the letter. It is from Dr. Pellerin, who is Jean's physician, who is his friend, our friend, a good fellow, a free liver, and a physician to many women of the world, and one who would not write such things unless necessity compelled him. [*Hands the letter to* Léon, *who holds it close to his eyes.*]

LÉON [*reads*]

"MY DEAR FRIEND:

"I am more than annoyed at having to communicate with you upon this evening, above every other evening, upon such a subject as this. But I am sure that if I did otherwise you would never forgive me. Your former mistress, Henriette Lévêque, is dying and would bid you farewell. [*Throws a glance at* Martinel *who signs to him to continue.*] She will not live through the night. She dies after bringing into the world, some fifteen days ago, a child who on her deathbed she swears is yours. So long as she was in no danger, she determined to leave you in ignorance of this child's existence. But, to-day, doomed to death, she calls to you. I know how you have loved her in the past. But you must do as you think fit. She lives in the Rue Chaptal at Number 31. Let me know how I can serve you, my dear fellow, and believe me,

"Always yours,

"PELLERIN."

MARTINEL

There you are. That letter came this evening. That is to say, at the one moment above all others when such a misfortune could threaten the whole future — the whole life of your sister and of Jean. What would you do if you were I? Would you keep this confounded letter, or would you give it to him? If I keep it, we may save appearances, but such an act would be unworthy of me.

LÉON [*energetically*]

I should say so. You must give the letter to Jean.

MARTINEL

Well, what will he do?

LÉON

He alone is the judge of his own actions. We have no right to hide anything from him.

MARTINEL

Supposing he consults me?

LÉON

He will not do it. In such situations a man consults only his conscience.

MARTINEL

But he treats me like a father. If he hesitates a moment between his attention to his wife and the effacement of his happiness, what shall I tell him to do?

LÉON

Just what you would do yourself in like case.

MARTINEL

My impulse would be to go to the woman. What would be yours?

LÉON [*resolutely*]

I should go.

MARTINEL

But how about your sister?

LÉON [*sadly, seating himself by the table*]

Yes, my poor little sister! What an awakening for her!

MARTINEL [*after a few seconds' hesitation, crosses abruptly from L. to R.*]

No; it is too hard a thing to do. I shall not give him this letter. I shall be blamed perhaps, but so much the worse. In any case, I save him.

LÉON

You cannot do such a thing, sir. We both know my sister, poor little girl, and I am sure that if this marriage is annulled, she will die. [*Rises.*] When a man has for three years enjoyed the love of such a woman as the one who sends for him, he cannot refuse to see her on her deathbed whatever may happen.

MARTINEL

What will Gilberte do?

14 G. de M.—9

LÉON

She worships Jean — but you know how proud she is.

MARTINEL

Will she accept the situation? Will she forgive it?

LÉON

Of that I am very doubtful, especially after all that has been said about this poor girl in the family circle. But what does that matter? Jean must be warned at once. I am going to find him and bring him to you. [*Rises as if to go out* C.]

MARTINEL

Well, how would you like me to tell him?

LÉON

Simply give him the letter.   [*Exit* Léon C.]

SCENE VII.

MARTINEL [*alone*]

Poor children! in the midst of their happiness and at the zenith of joy! And that other poor girl, who is now suffering and slowly dying! Heavens! How unjust and how cruel life is at times.

Scene VIII.

(*Re-enter* Léon *with* Jean)

JEAN [*walks briskly to* C. *of stage*]
What is it all about?

MARTINEL

One minute, my poor boy; read this, and forgive me for having opened your letter. I opened it because I thought it was intended for me. [*Gives letter to* Jean, *and watches him read it.* Léon *also watches him, standing* L.]

JEAN [*after reading the letter, speaks to himself in a low tone, touched with deep but contained emotion*]

I must do it! I owe it to her! [*To Martinel.*] Uncle, I leave my wife in your charge. Say nothing until I return, and remain here till I come back. Wait for me. [*Turns to* Léon.] I know you well enough to realize that you do not disapprove of what I am doing. To you I confide my future. I am going. [*Turns to the door* R., *but after casting a glance at the door* L., *which leads to his wife's chamber, says to* Léon.] To you I owe the love your sister has bestowed upon me. Help me now to preserve it.

[*Exit quickly* R.

SCENE IX.

(Martinel *and* Léon.)

MARTINEL [*seated* R.]

What shall we do now? What are we going to say? What explanations can we give?

LÉON

Let me manage it. It is only right that I should do it since I brought about this marriage.

MARTINEL [*rises*]

Well, I'd dearly love to be forty-eight hours older. [*Rising.*] I confess I do not like these love trage-dies, and moreover the fact of the child entering into the case is awful. What is going to become of that poor little mortal? We cannot send him to the foundling asylum. [*Enter* Gilberte L.] Gilberte!

SCENE X.

Gilberte *has removed her marriage robes, and now wears a handsome house gown. She carries an opera cloak, which she throws over a chair near the door.*

GILBERTE

Where is Jean?

LÉON

Do not be disturbed, he will be back directly.

GILBERTE [*in astonishment*]

Has he gone out?

LÉON

Yes.

GILBERTE

Gone out? And on this evening, above all others!

LÉON

A sudden and grave circumstance compelled him to go out for an hour.

GILBERTE [*excitedly*]

What is going on? What is it that you are hiding from me? Your story is impossible. Some awful misfortune must have happened.

LÉON AND MARTINEL [*together*]

Oh, no, no!

GILBERTE

Then, what is it? Tell me! Speak!

LÉON

I cannot tell you anything. Be patient for an hour. It is Jean's duty to tell you of the sudden and unexpected call which has summoned him hence at such a time.

GILBERTE

What curious words you use! A sudden and unexpected call? He is an orphan—his uncle is his only relative,—then what? Who? Why? Oh, God, how you frighten me!

LÉON

There are duties of many kinds, my dear; friendship, pity, sympathy can impose many of them. But I must not say any more. Be patient for an hour, I implore you.

GILBERTE [*to* Martinel]

And you, Uncle? Speak! I implore you! What is he doing? Where has he gone? I feel—oh, I feel the shadow of a terrible misfortune hovering over us; speak, I entreat.

MARTINEL [*with tears in his eyes*]

But I cannot tell you any more, my dear child. I cannot. Like your brother, I promised to say nothing, and I would have done just as Jean has done. Wait for an hour, I beseech you—just an hour.

GILBERTE

And you, too, are upset. It must be a catastrophe.

MARTINEL

No, no! The fact that you are so distressed agitates me, because you know I love you with my whole heart. [*Embraces her.*]

GILBERTE [*to* Léon]

You have spoken of friendship, of pity, and of sympathy, but if it were any of these reasons you could tell me so; meanwhile, as I look at you two, I feel that here is some unspoken reason, some mystery which appalls me.

LÉON [*resolutely*]

My dear little sister, won't you trust in me?

GILBERTE

Yes, you ought to know all.

LÉON

Will you trust me absolutely?

GILBERTE

Absolutely.

LÉON

I swear to you, on my faith as a gentleman, that I would have done just as Jean has done; that his absolute fidelity to you, his fidelity, which perhaps is even exaggerated by love for you, is the only reason which had led him to forget at this very moment the very thing that he has gone to learn anew.

GILBERTE [*looks* Léon *straight in the eyes*]

I believe you, Léon, and I thank you. Nevertheless, I tremble yet and I shall tremble until he returns. If you swear to me that my husband was entirely ignorant of the cause which has made him

leave me at this supreme moment, I will content myself as well as I can, trusting in you two. [*She
stretches both hands to the two men.*]

Scene XI.

(*The same, with* M. de Petitpré *and* Mme. de
Ronchard, *who enters quickly* C.)

PETITPRÉ

What is this I hear? Jean Martinel gone out?

MARTINEL

He is coming back very soon, sir.

PETITPRÉ

But why on earth did he go out on such an evening as this without a word of explanation to his
wife? [*Turns to* Gilberte] You know nothing about
it, do you?

GILBERTE [*seated* L. *of table*]

Father, I know nothing at all about it.

MME. DE RONCHARD

And without a word of explanation to the family!
That is indeed a lack of courtesy.

PETITPRÉ [*to* Martinel]

And why has he acted in this way, sir?

MARTINEL

Your son knows as much as I do, sir; but neither of us can reveal it to you. Moreover, your daughter has consented to wait until she can learn all about it from her husband on his return.

PETITPRÉ

My daughter has consented — but I do not consent! Besides, it seems that you alone were forewarned of this sudden departure.

MME. DE RONCHARD [*in agitation to* Martinel]

It was to you they brought the letter, and you were the one who read it first.

MARTINEL

You are correctly informed, Madame; a letter was delivered here, but I would not shoulder the responsibility of this matter, and I showed the letter to your son, sir [*turns to* Petitpré], and asked his advice with the intention of following it.

LÉON

The advice that I gave is exactly what my brother-in-law has done of his own volition, and I esteem him all the more for it.

PETITPRÉ [*turns to* Léon]

It is I who should have been consulted, not you. If Jean's action is indeed excusable, his want of courtesy is absolutely unpardonable.

MME. DE RONCHARD

It is scandalous!

LÉON [*to* M. Petitpré]

Yes, it would have been better to consult you, but the urgency of the matter did not allow it. You would have discussed the matter; my aunt would have discussed the matter; we should all have discussed the matter the whole night long, and you know there are times when one cannot afford to lose even seconds. Silence was necessary until Jean's return. When he does return he will hide nothing from you, and I feel sure that you will judge him as I myself have judged him.

MME. DE RONCHARD [*turns to* Martinel]

But this letter, from whom did it come?

MARTINEL

Oh, I can tell you that. It came from a physician.

MME. DE RONCHARD

From a physician — a physician — then he must have a sick patient — and it is on account of this patient that he made Jean come to him. But who is the patient? Oh, ho! I surmise that it is a woman — that woman — his former mistress, who has played this card to-day. Sick! I suppose she has made a pretense of poisoning herself in order to show him that she loves him still and will always love him. Oh, the little wretch! [*To* Léon.] This is the kind of people you stand up for! Yes, you!

LÉON

It would be only reasonable, my dear Aunt, not to air all these revolting theories of yours in Gilberte's presence, especially when you really know nothing at all.

GILBERTE [*rises*]

Do not speak any more about it, I pray you. Everything that I have heard just now distresses me beyond measure. I will wait for my husband; I do not wish to know anything except from his lips, as I have absolute confidence in him. If misfortune has threatened us, I will not hear such things talked of. [*Exit* L, *accompanied by* Petitpré. *Short silence.*]

MME. DE RONCHARD [*turns to* Léon]

Well, Léon, do you always win? You see what charming fellows these husbands are—every one of them!

ACT II.

Scene I.

Musotte's *bedroom, neatly furnished, but without luxury. Disordered bed stands* L. *A screen stands* L. I. E., *almost hiding* Musotte, *who lies stretched at length upon a steamer-chair. Beside the bed is a cradle, the head of which is turned up stage. On the mantelpiece and on small tables at* R. *and* L. *are vials of medicine, cups, chafing-dish, etc. A table stands* R. I. E. Musotte *is sleeping.* La Babin *and* Mme. Flache *stand* C. *looking at her.*

LA BABIN [*in low tones*]

How she sleeps!

MME. FLACHE [*in the same voice*]

But she will not sleep long now, unless she is going into her last sleep.

LA BABIN

Oh, there is no chance of that. That is enough to give one the horrors. Fancy losing one's life for a child!

MME. FLACHE

But how can you prevent it? Death is as necessary as birth, or the world would become too small for us all.

(50)

LA BABIN [*sits* R. *of table*]

All people ought to die in the same way and at the same age — every one of us; then one would know what to expect.

MME. FLACHE [*pours out some tea*]

What simple ideas you have, Madame Babin! Personally, I would rather not know the hour of my death. I would sooner finish my life while sleeping in the middle of the night — during slumber — without suffering — by a sudden failure of the heart.

LA BABIN

Look at the sick woman. How silly of her to wish to rest upon that steamer-chair as she has done. The doctor told her plainly that such an effort would probably finish her.

MME. FLACHE [*sits* L. *of table*]

Oh, I understand her motive. When a girl like her has a lover she commits every kind of folly, and more especially, nurse, when they are at all coquettish; but you country people do not know anything about such things. They are coquettish through and through. That is the reason she wished to look her prettiest. She was afraid of being thought ugly, don't you understand? So I had to put on her *peignoir*, and tidy her up, and arrange her hair just as I have done.

LA BABIN

Oh, these Parisians! It is necessary that they should have a hairdresser even to the last gasp! [*A short silence.*] But will this gentleman of hers come?

MME. FLACHE

I do not think so. Men are not overfond of obeying the calls of their former mistresses at such times, and then, this lover of hers was married to-day, poor fellow!

LA BABIN

Well, that is a joke.

MME. FLACHE

I should say so.

LA BABIN

Certainly, then, he won't come. In such a case would *you* go to see a man?

MME. FLACHE

Oh, if I loved him very much I should go.

LA BABIN

Even if you were marrying another the same day?

MME. FLACHE

Just the same. For such a combination of circumstances would pierce my heart; would penetrate me with a strong emotion,—and, oh, I am so fond of such emotions!

LA BABIN

Well, so far as I am concerned, I certainly would not go. I should be too much afraid of the shock.

MME. FLACHE

But Doctor Pellerin asserts that the man will come.

LA BABIN

Do you know this physician well?

MME. FLACHE

Who, Doctor Pellerin?

LA BABIN

Yes; he has the air of a charming man of the world.

MME. FLACHE

Oh, yes; he is all that, but he is also a good physician. Then he is such good company, and has such a smooth tongue. And you know he is not physician to the Opera for nothing.

LA BABIN

That little puppy of a —

MME. FLACHE

A puppy! You don't very often find puppies among men of his caliber, and then,—oh, how he used to love the girls! Oh, oh! Although, for the matter of that, there are many physicians who are like him. It was at the Opera that I first met him.

LA BABIN

At the Opera!

MME. FLACHE

Yes, at the Opera. You know, I was a dancer there for eight years. Yes, indeed, even I—just as you see me, a dancer at the Opera.

LA BABIN

You, Madame Flache!

MME. FLACHE

Yes, my mother was a midwife, and taught me the business at the same time that she taught me dancing, because she always said it was well to have two strings to your bow. Dancing, you see, is all very well, provided you are not too ambitious of appearing on first nights, but, unhappily, that was the case with me. I was as slender as a thread when I was twenty, and very agile, but I grew fat and scant of breath, and became rather heavy in my steps; so when my mother died, as I had my diploma as a midwife, I took her apartment and her business, and I added the title of "Midwife to the Opera," for all their business comes to me. They like me very much there. When I was dancing, they used to call me Mademoiselle Flacchi the première.

LA BABIN

Then you have been married since then?

MME. FLACHE

No, but a woman in my profession should always assume the title of Madame for the sake of its dignity. You know, it gives confidence. But, how about you, nurse, from what place do you come? You know, you have only just come here, and nobody consulted me about engaging you.

LA BABIN

I am from Yvetot.

MME. FLACHE

Is this your first engagement as a nurse?

LA BABIN

No, my third. I have had two daughters and a little boy.

MME. FLACHE

And your husband, is he a farmer or a gardener?

LA BABIN [*simply*]

I am not married.

MME. FLACHE [*laughing*]

Not married, and with three children! Upon my word, let me compliment you; you are indeed precocious.

LA BABIN

Don't talk about it; it was not my will. It is the good God who does these things. One cannot prevent it.

MME. FLACHE

How simple you are! Now you will probably have a fourth child.

LA BABIN

That's very possible.

MME. FLACHE

Well, what does your lover do? What is his business? Or perhaps you have more than one?

LA BABIN [*with indignation*]

There has never been more than one. I give you my word, upon my hope of salvation. He is a lemonade-seller at Yvetot.

MME. FLACHE

Is he a handsome fellow?

LA BABIN

I believe you, indeed! He is handsome! [*Confidentially.*] If I tell you all this, it is only because you are a midwife, and a midwife in such affairs as this is like a priest in the confessional. But you, Madame Flache, you, who have been a dancer at the Opera, you must also have had, surely — little love affairs — little intrigues?

MME. FLACHE [*evidently flattered, and in a dreamy tone*]

Oh, yes, one or two!

LA BABIN [*laughs*]

And have you never had — this sort of accident? [*Points to the cradle.*]

MME. FLACHE

No.

LA BABIN

How did that come?

MME. FLACHE [*rises and approaches the mantelpiece*]

Probably because I was a midwife.

LA BABIN

Well, I know one in your profession who has had five.

MME. FLACHE [*with contempt*]

She evidently did not come from Paris.

LA BABIN

That's true; she came from Courbevoie.

MUSOTTE [*in a feeble voice*]

Is no one there?

MME. FLACHE

She is awakening. There, there! [*Folds up the screen which hides the long steamer-chair.*]

MUSOTTE

Hasn't he come yet?

MME. FLACHE

No.

MUSOTTE

He will arrive too late—my God! My God!

MME. FLACHE

What an idea! He will come.

MUSOTTE

And my little darling—my child?

MME. FLACHE

He is sleeping like an angel.

MUSOTTE [*after looking at herself in a hand-mirror*]

I must not look like this when he comes. Oh, God! Bring my child—I want to see him.

MME. FLACHE

But if I show him to you he will wake up, and who knows if he will go to sleep again.

MUSOTTE

Bring the cradle here. [*A gesture of refusal from* Mme Flache.] Yes, yes! I insist. [Mme. Flache *and the nurse gently bring the cradle to her.*] Nearer, nearer, so that I can see him well—the darling! My child, my child! And I am going to leave him! Soon I shall disappear into the unknown. Oh, God, what agony!

MME. FLACHE

Now, don't go worrying yourself like that; you are not as ill as you think. I have seen lots worse than you. Come, come! you are going to recover. Take away the cradle, nurse. [*They put the cradle again in its place; then to the nurse.*] That will do, that will do. Watch me. You know very well that it is only I who can quiet it. [*Sits near the cradle, and sings a lullaby while rocking it.*]

> "A little gray fowl
> Came into the barn,
> To lay a big egg
> For the good boy that sleeps.
> Go to sleep, go to sleep,
> My little chicken!
> Go to sleep, sleep, my chick!"

LA BABIN [*stands near the end of the mantelpiece, drinks the sugared water, and slips loaf sugar into her pocket; aside*]

I must not forget the main thing. I have just seen in the kitchen the remains of a leg of mutton, to which I should like to go and say a few words. I am breaking in two with hunger just now.

MME. FLACHE [*sings softly*]

"A little black fowl
Came into the room,
To lay a big egg
For the good boy that sleeps.
Sleep, sleep, my little chicken,
Sleep, oh, sleep, my chick!"

MUSOTTE [*from the long chair, after moaning several times*]

Has he gone to sleep again?

MME. FLACHE [*goes toward* Musotte]

Yes, Mademoiselle, just as if he were a little Jesus. Do you wish to know what I think about him, this young man lying here? You will lead him to the altar for his marriage. He is a jewel, like yourself, my dear.

MUSOTTE

Do you really think him pretty?

MME. FLACHE

On the honor of a midwife, I have seldom brought into the world one so pretty. It is a pleasure to know that one has brought to the light such a little Cupid as he is.

MUSOTTE

And to think that in a few hours, perhaps, I shall see him no more; look at him no more; love him no more!

MME. FLACHE

Oh, no, no! You are talking unreasonably.

MUSOTTE

Ah, I know it too well! I heard you talking with the nurse. I know that the end is very near; this night, perhaps. Would the doctor have written to Jean to come and see me on this evening — the evening of his marriage — if I were not at the point of death? [*The bell rings.* Musotte *utters a cry.*] Ah, there he is! it is he! Quick! quick! Oh, God, how I suffer! [*Exit* Mme. Flache C. Musotte *gazes after her. Enter* Dr. Pellerin, *in evening clothes.*]

SCENE II.

MUSOTTE [*despairingly*]

Ah! it is not he!

PELLERIN [*approaches* Musotte]

Has he not come yet?

MUSOTTE

He will not come.

DR. PELLERIN

He will! I am certain of it; I know it.

MUSOTTE

No!

DR. PELLERIN

I swear it! [*Turns toward* Mme. Flache.] Hasn't
he answered the note yet?

MME. FLACHE

No, Doctor.

DR. PELLERIN

Well, he will come. How is my patient?

MME. FLACHE

She has rested a little.

MUSOTTE [*in an agitated voice*]

All is over! I feel that I shall not rest any more
until he comes, or until I depart without having seen
him.

DR. PELLERIN

He will come if you will go to sleep immediately
and sleep until to-morrow morning.

MUSOTTE

You would not have written to him to come this
evening if I had been able to wait until to-morrow
morning. [*The bell rings.*] If that is not he, I am
lost—lost! [Mme. Flache *runs to open the door.*
Musotte *listens intently, and hears from below a man's
voice; then murmurs despairingly.*] It is not he!

MME. FLACHE [*re-enters with a vial in her hand*]

It is the medicine from the chemist.

MUSOTTE [*agitated*]

Oh, God! how horrible! He is not coming; what have I done? Doctor, show me my child. I will see him once more.

DR. PELLERIN

But he sleeps, my little Musotte.

MUSOTTE

Well, he has plenty of time in the future for sleep.

DR. PELLERIN

Come, come, calm yourself.

MUSOTTE

If Jean does not come, who will take care of my child?—for it is Jean's child, I swear to you. Do you believe me? Oh, how I loved him!

DR. PELLERIN

Yes, my dear little child, we believe you. But please be calm.

MUSOTTE [*with increasing agitation*]

Tell me, when you went away just now where did you go?

DR. PELLERIN

To see a patient.

MUSOTTE

That is not true. You went to see Jean, and he would not come with you, or he would be here now.

DR. PELLERIN

On my word of honor, no.

MUSOTTE

Yes, I feel it. You have seen him, and you do not dare to tell me for fear it would kill me.

DR. PELLERIN

Ah, the fever is coming back again. This must not go on. I don't wish you to be delirious when he comes. [*Turns to* Mme. Flache.] We must give her a hypodermic injection. Give me the morphia. [Mme. Flache *brings the needle and morphia from the mantelpiece and gives it to* Dr. Pellerin.]

MUSOTTE [*uncovers her own arm*]

But for this relief, I do not know how I should have borne up during the last few days. [Dr. Pellerin *administers the hypodermic.*]

DR. PELLERIN

Now, you must go to sleep; I forbid you to speak. I won't answer you, and I tell you of a certainty that in a quarter of an hour Jean will be here. [Musotte *stretches herself out obediently upon the couch and goes to sleep.*]

LA BABIN [*silently replaces the screen which hides* Musotte]

How she sleeps! What a benediction that drug is! But I don't want any of it. It scares me; it is a devil's potion. [*Sits near the cradle and reads a newspaper.*]

MME. FLACHE [*in a low voice to* Dr. Pellerin]

Oh, the poor girl, what misery!

DR. PELLERIN [*in the same tone*]

Yes, she is a brave girl. It is some time since I first met her with Jean Martinel, who gave her three years of complete happiness. She has a pure and simple soul.

MME. FLACHE

Well, will this Monsieur Martinel come?

DR. PELLERIN

I think so. He is a man of feeling, but it is a difficult thing for him to leave his wife and his people on such a day as this.

MME. FLACHE

It certainly is a most extraordinary case. A veritable *fiasco*.

DR. PELLERIN

It is, indeed.

MME. FLACHE [*changes her tone*]

Where have you been just now? You did not put on evening dress and a white cravat to go and see a patient?

DR. PELLERIN

I went to see the first part of the Montargy ballet danced.

MME. FLACHE [*interested, and leaning upon the edge of the table*]

And was it good? Tell me.

DR. PELLERIN [*sits L. of table*]

It was very well danced.

MME. FLACHE

The new directors do things in style, don't they?

DR. PELLERIN

Jeanne Merali and Gabrielle Poivrier are first class.

MME. FLACHE

Poivrier—the little Poivrier—is it possible! As to Merali I am not so much astonished; although she is distinctly ugly, she has her good points. And how about Mauri?

DR. PELLERIN

Oh, a marvel—an absolute marvel, who dances as no one else can. A human bird with limbs for wings. It was absolute perfection.

MME. FLACHE

Are you in love with her?

DR. PELLERIN

Oh, no; merely an admirer. You know how I worship the dance.

MME. FLACHE

And the *danseuses* also, at times. [*Lowering her eyes.*] Come, have you forgotten?

DR. PELLERIN

One can never forget artists of your worth, my
dear.

MME. FLACHE

You are simply teasing me.

DR. PELLERIN

I only do you justice.   You know that formerly,
when I was a young doctor, I had for you a very
ardent passion which lasted six weeks.   Tell me,
don't you regret the time of the grand *fête*?

MME. FLACHE

A little.   But reason comes when one is young
no longer, and I have nothing to complain of.   My
business is very prosperous.

DR. PELLERIN

You are making money, then?   They tell me that
you are giving dainty little dinners.

MME. FLACHE

I believe you, and I have a particularly good
chef.   Won't you give me the pleasure of entertaining you at dinner one of these days, my dear
Doctor?

DR. PELLERIN

Very willingly, my dear.

MME. FLACHE

Shall I have any other physicians, or do you prefer to come alone?

DR. PELLERIN

Alone, if you please. I am not fond of a third party. [*The bell rings.*]

MUSOTTE [*awakens*]

Ah, some one rang, run and see. [*Exit* Mme. Flache. *A short silence.*]

A VOICE [*without*]

Madame Henriette Lévêque?

MUSOTTE [*emitting an anguished cry*]

Ah, it is he! There he is! [*Makes an effort to rise. Enter* Jean Martinel.] Jean! Jean! At last! [*Springs up and stretches her arms to him.*]

SCENE III.

(*The same, with* Jean Martinel.)

JEAN [*comes rapidly forward, kneels near the long steamer-chair, and kisses* Musotte's *hands*]

My poor little Musotte! [*They begin to weep and dry their eyes; then they remain silent and motionless. At last* Jean *rises and holds up his hand to* Dr. Pellerin.]

PELLERIN

Did I do well?

JEAN

You did indeed, and I thank you.

PELLERIN [*introduces them*]

Madame Flache, the midwife—the nurse—[*indicates the cradle with a grave gesture*] and there!

JEAN [*approaches the cradle and lifts the little curtain, takes up the child and kisses it on the mouth; then lays it down again*]

He is a splendid boy!

DR. PELLERIN

A very pretty child.

MME. FLACHE

A superb morsel — one of my prettiest.

JEAN [*in a low voice*]

And Musotte, how is she?

MUSOTTE [*who has heard him*]

I,— I am almost lost. I know surely that all is over. [*To* Jean.] Take that little chair, dear, and seat yourself near me, and let us talk as long as I am able to speak. I have so many things to say to you, for we shall never be together any more. I am so glad to see you again that nothing else now seems of any importance.

JEAN [*approaching her*]

Don't agitate yourself. Don't get excited.

MUSOTTE

How can I help being agitated at seeing you again?

JEAN [*sits on the low chair, takes* Musotte's *hand*]

My poor Musotte, I cannot tell you what a shock it was to me when I learned just now that you were so ill.

MUSOTTE

And on this day of all days! It must have shocked you greatly.

JEAN

What! Do you know of it then?

MUSOTTE

Yes, since I felt so ill, I kept myself informed about you every day, in order that I might not pass away without having seen you and spoken to you again, for I have so much to say to you. [*At a sign from* Jean, Mme. Flache, Pellerin, *and* La Babin *exit* R.]

SCENE IV.

(Musotte *and* Jean.)

MUSOTTE

Then you received the letter?

JEAN

Yes.

MUSOTTE

And you came immediately?

JEAN

Certainly.

MUSOTTE

Thanks — ah! thanks. I hesitated a long time before warning you — hesitated even this morning, but I heard the midwife talking with the nurse and learned that to-morrow perhaps it might be too late, so I sent Doctor Pellerin to call you immediately.

JEAN

Why didn't you call me sooner?

MUSOTTE

I never thought that my illness would become so serious. I did not wish to trouble your life.

JEAN [*points to the cradle*]

But that child! How is it that I was not told of this sooner?

MUSOTTE

You would never have known it, if his birth had not killed me. I would have spared you this pain — this cloud upon your life. When you left me, you gave me enough to live upon. Everything was over between us; and besides, at any other moment than this, would you believe me if I said to you: "This is your child?"

JEAN

Yes, I have never doubted you.

MUSOTTE

You are as good as ever, my Jean. No, no, I am not lying to you; he is yours that little one there. I swear it to you on my deathbed; I swear it to you before God!

JEAN

I have already told you that I believed you. I have always believed you.

MUSOTTE

Listen, this is all that has happened. As soon as you left me, I became very ill. I suffered so much that I thought I was going to die. The doctor ordered a change of air. You remember, it was in the spring. I went to Saint-Malo — to that old relative, of whom I have often talked to you.

JEAN

Yes, yes.

MUSOTTE

It was in Saint-Malo, after some days, that I realized that you had left me a pledge of your affection. My first desire was to tell you everything, for I knew that you were an honest man — that you would have recognized this child, perhaps even have given up your marriage; but I would not have had you do that. All was over; was it not? — and it was better that it should be so. I knew that I could never be your wife [*smiles*], Musotte, me, Madame Martinel — oh, no!

14 G. de M.—11

JEAN

My poor, dear girl. How brutal and hard we men are, without thinking of it and without wishing to be so!

MUSOTTE

Don't say that. I was not made for you. I was only a little model; and you, you were a rising artist, and I never thought that you would belong to me forever. [Jean *sheds tears.*] No, no, don't cry; you have nothing to reproach yourself with. You have always been so good to me. It is only God who has been cruel to me.

JEAN

Musotte!

MUSOTTE

Let me go on. I remained at Saint-Malo without revealing my condition. Then I came back to Paris, and here some months afterward the little one was born — the child! When I fully understood what had happened to me, I experienced at first such fear; yes, such fear! Then I remembered that he was bone of your bone, and flesh of your flesh; that you had given him life, and that he was a pledge from you. But one is so stupid when one knows nothing. One's ideas change just as one's moods change, and I became contented all at once; contented with the thought that I would bring him up, that he would grow to be a man, that he would call me mother. [*Weeps.*] Now, he will never call me mother. He will never put his little arms around my neck, because I am going to leave him; because I am going away—I don't know where; but there, where everybody goes. Oh, God! My God!

JEAN

Calm yourself, my little Musotte. Would you be able to speak as you do speak if you were as ill as you think you are?

MUSOTTE

You do not see that the fever is burning within me; that I am losing my head, and don't know longer what I say.

JEAN

No, no; please calm yourself.

MUSOTTE

Pet me; pet me, Jean, and you will calm me.

JEAN [kisses her hair; then resumes]

There, there; don't speak any more for a minute or two. Let us remain quietly here near each other.

MUSOTTE

But I must speak to you; I have so many things to say to you yet, and do not know how to say them. My head is beyond my control. Oh, my God! how shall I do it? [Raises herself, looks around her and sees the cradle.] Ah, yes, I know; I recollect, it is he, my child. Tell me, Jean, what will you do with him? You know that I am an orphan, and when I am gone he will be here all alone—alone in the world! Poor little thing! Listen, Jean, my head is quite clear now. I shall understand very well what you answer me now, and the peace of my closing moments depends upon it. I have no one to leave the little one to but you.

JEAN

I promise you that I will take him, look after him, and bring him up.

MUSOTTE

As a father?

JEAN

As a father.

MUSOTTE

You have already seen him?

JEAN

Yes.

MUSOTTE

Go and look at him again. [Jean *goes over to the cradle.*]

JEAN

He is pretty, isn't he?

MUSOTTE

Everybody says so. Look at him, the poor little darling, who has enjoyed only a few days of life as yet. He belongs to us. You are his father; I am his mother, but soon he will have a mother no more. [*In anguish.*] Promise me that he shall always have a father.

JEAN [*goes over to her*]

I promise it, my darling!

MUSOTTE

A *true* father, who will always love him well?

JEAN

I promise it.

MUSOTTE

You will be good — very good — to him?

JEAN

I swear it to you!

MUSOTTE

And then, there is something else — but I dare
not —

JEAN

Tell it to me.

MUSOTTE

Since I came back to Paris, I have sought to see
you without being seen by you, and I have seen you
three times. Each time you were with her — with
your sweetheart, your wife, and with a gentleman —
her father, I think. Oh, how I looked at her! I asked
myself: "Will she love him as I have loved him?
Will she make him happy? Is she good?" Tell me,
do you really believe she is very good?

JEAN

Yes, darling, I believe it.

MUSOTTE

You are very certain of it?

JEAN

Yes, indeed.

MUSOTTE

And I thought so, too, simply from seeing her pass by. She is so pretty! I have been a little jealous, and I wept on coming back. But what are you going to do now as between her and your son?

JEAN

I shall do my duty.

MUSOTTE

Your duty? Does that mean by her or by him?

JEAN

By him.

MUSOTTE

Listen, Jean: when I am no more, ask your wife from me, from the mouth of a dead woman, to adopt him, this dear little morsel of humanity — to love him as I would have loved him; to be a mother to him in my stead. If she is tender and kind, she will consent. Tell her how you saw me suffer — that my last prayer, my last supplication on earth was offered up for her. Will you do this?

JEAN

I promise you that I will.

MUSOTTE

Ah! How good you are! Now I fear nothing; my poor little darling is safe, and I am happy and calm. Ah, how calm I am! You didn't know, did you, that I called him Jean, after you? That does not displease you, does it?

JEAN [*weeps*]

No, no!

MUSOTTE

You weep—so you still love me a little, Jean? Ah, how I thank you for this! But if I only could live; it must be possible. I feel so much better since you came here, and since you have promised me all that I have asked you. Give me your hand. At this moment I can recall all our life together, and I am content—almost gay; in fact, I can laugh—see, I can laugh, though I don't know why. [*Laughs.*]

JEAN

Oh, calm yourself for my sake, dear little Musotte.

MUSOTTE

If you could only understand how recollections throng upon me. Do you remember that I posed for your "Mendiante," for your "Violet Seller," for your "Guilty Woman," which won for you your first medal? And do you remember the breakfast at Ledoyen's on Varnishing Day? There were more than twenty-five at a table intended for ten. What follies we committed, especially that little, little—what did he call himself—I mean that little comic fellow, who was always making portraits which resembled no one? Oh, yes, Tavernier! And you took me home with you to your studio, where you had two great manikins which frightened me so, and I called to you, and you came in to reassure me. Oh, how heavenly all that was! Do you remember? [*Laughs again.*] Oh, if that life could only begin over again! [*Cries suddenly.*] Ah, what pain! [*To* Jean, *who is going for the doctor.*] No, stay, stay! [*Silence. A sudden change comes over her face.*] See, Jean, what glorious weather! If you like, we will take the baby for a sail on a river steamboat; that will be so jolly! I love those little steamboats; they are so pretty. They glide over the water quickly and without noise. Now that I am your wife, I can assert myself—I am armed. Darling, I never thought that you would marry me. And look at our little one—how pretty he is, and how he grows! He is called Jean after you. And I—I have my two little Jeans—mine—altogether mine! You don't know how happy I am. And the little one walks to-day for the first time! [*Laughs aloud, with her arms stretched out, pointing to the child which she thinks is before her.*]

JEAN [*weeps*]

Musotte! Musotte! Don't you know me?

MUSOTTE

Indeed I know you! Am I not your wife? Kiss me, darling. Kiss me, my little one.

JEAN [*takes her in his arms, weeping and repeating*]

Musotte! Musotte! [Musotte *rises upon her couch, and with a gesture to* Jean *points to the cradle,*

AFTER AN ORIGINAL DRAWING BY J. C. FIREMAN.

"Kiss me, darling! Kiss me."

toward which he goes, nodding " Yes, yes," with his head. When Jean *reaches the cradle,* Musotte, *who has raised herself upon her hands, falls lifeless upon the long steamer-chair.* Jean, *frightened, calls out*] Pellerin! Pellerin!

Scene V.

(*The same:* Pellerin, Mme. Flache, *and* La Babin, *enter quickly* R.)

PELLERIN [*who has gone swiftly to* Musotte, *feels her pulse and listens at the heart*]

Her heart is not beating! Give me a mirror, Madame Flache.

JEAN

My God! [Mme. Flache *gives a hand-mirror to* Pellerin, *who holds it before the lips of* Musotte. *Pause.*]

PELLERIN [*in a low voice*]

She is dead!

JEAN [*takes the dead woman's hand and kisses it fondly, his voice choked with emotion*]

Farewell, my dear little Musotte! To think that a moment ago you were speaking to me — a moment ago you were looking at me, you saw me, and now — all is over!

PELLERIN [*goes to* Jean *and takes him by the shoulder*]

Now, you must go at once. Go! You have nothing more to do here. Your duty is over.

JEAN [*rises*]

I go. Farewell, poor little Musotte!

PELLERIN

I will take care of everything this evening. But the child, do you wish me to find an asylum for him?

JEAN

Oh, no, I will take him. I have sworn it to that poor, dead darling. Come and join me immediately at my house, and bring him with you. Then I shall have another service to request of you. But how about Musotte, who is going to remain with her?

MME. FLACHE

I, Monsieur. Have no anxiety; I am acquainted with all that must be done.

JEAN

Thank you, Madame. [*Approaches the bed; closes* Musotte's *eyes and kisses her fondly and for a long time upon her forehead.*] Farewell, Musotte, forever! [*Goes softly to the cradle, removes the veil, kisses the child and speaks to it in a firm voice which at the same time is full of tears.*] I shall see you again directly, my little Jean!   [*Exit quickly.*

ACT III.

Scene I.

(*Same setting as in* Act I.)

(Monsieur de Petitpré, Mme. de Ronchard, M. Martinel, *and* Léon.)

MME. DE RONCHARD [*walks about in an agitated manner*]

SEVEN minutes to midnight! It is nearly two hours since Jean left us!

LÉON [*seated L.*]

But, my dear Aunt, just allow a half hour in the carriage for going and a half hour for returning, and there remains just one hour for the business he had to attend to.

MME. DE RONCHARD

Was it so very long, then—the business that called him hence?

LÉON

Yes, my dear Aunt; and now, why worry yourself by counting the minutes? Your agitation will

(81)

change nothing in the end, and will not hasten Jean's return by a single second, or make the hands of the clock move more quickly.

MME. DE RONCHARD

How can you ask me not to worry when my mind is full of anxiety, when my heart is beating, and I feel the tears rising into my eyes?

LÉON

But, my dear Aunt, you know very well you do not feel as badly as that.

MME. DE RONCHARD

Oh, you irritate me!

MARTINEL [*seated near the table*]

Don't torment yourself, Madame. True, the situation is a rather delicate one, but it need not disquiet you or frighten us, if we know how to bring to its consideration at this moment coolness and reason.

LÉON

Just so, my dear Aunt, Monsieur Martinel speaks truly.

MME. DE RONCHARD [*crossés* R.]

You ought to be beaten, you two! You know everything, and won't tell anything. How annoying men are! There is never any means of making them tell a secret.

MARTINEL

Jean will come presently and will tell you everything. Have a little patience.

PETITPRÉ

Yes; let us be calm. Let us talk of other things,
or be silent, if we can.

MME. DE RONCHARD

Be silent! That is about the most difficult thing —

A SERVANT [*enters* R.]

A gentleman wishes to see M. Martinel.

MARTINEL [*rises*]

Pardon me for a moment. [*To the servant.*]
Very well, I am coming.   [*Exit* R.

SCENE II.

MME. DE RONCHARD [*approaches servant quickly*]

Baptiste, Baptiste! Who is asking for M. Martinel?

SERVANT

I do not know, Madame. It was the hall porter
who came upstairs.

MME. DE RONCHARD

Well, run now and look without showing yourself, and come back and tell us at once.

PETITPRÉ [*who has risen at the entrance of the servant*]

No, I will permit no spying; let us wait. We shall not have to wait long now. [*To the servant.*] You may go.   [*Exit servant.*

MME. DE RONCHARD [*to* Petitpré]

I do not understand you at all. You are absolutely calm. One would think that your daughter's happiness was nothing to you. For myself, I am profoundly agitated.

PETITPRÉ

That will do no good. [*Sits near the table* R.] Let us talk — talk reasonably, now that we are a family party and Monsieur Martinel is absent.

MME. DE RONCHARD [*Sits* R.]

If that man would only go back to Havre!

LÉON [*Sits* L. *of table*]

That would not change anything even if he could go back to Havre.

PETITPRÉ

For my part, I think —

MME. DE RONCHARD [*interrupts*]

Do you wish to hear my opinion? Well, I think that they are preparing us for some unpleasant surprise; that they wish to entrap us, as one might say.

PETITPRÉ

But why? In whose interest? Jean Martinel is
an honest man, and he loves my child. Léon, whose
judgment I admire, although he is my son —

LÉON

Thank you, father!

PETITPRÉ

Léon bears Jean as much affection as esteem. As
to the uncle —

MME. DE RONCHARD

Don't talk about them, I pray. It is this woman
who is seeking to entrap us. She has played some
little comedy, and she chooses to-day above all others
for its *dénouement*. It is her stage climax; her
masterpiece of treachery.

LÉON

As in "The Ambigu."

MME. DE RONCHARD   .

Do not laugh. I know these women. I have
suffered enough at their hands.

PETITPRÉ

Oh, my poor Clarisse; if you really understood
them, you would have held your husband better than
you did.

MME. DE RONCHARD [*rises*]

What do you mean by "understanding" them?
Pardon me — to live with that roisterer coming in

upon me when and whence he pleased — I prefer my
broken life and my loneliness — with you!

PETITPRÉ

No doubt you are right from your point of view
of a married woman; but there are other points of
view, perhaps less selfish and certainly superior, such
as that of family interest.

MME. DE RONCHARD

Of family interest, indeed? Do you mean to say
that I was wrong from the point of view of the
family interest — you, a magistrate!

PETITPRÉ

My duties as a magistrate have made me very
prudent, for I have seen pass under my eyes many
equivocal and terrible situations, which not only
agonized my conscience but gave me many cruel
hours of indecision. Man is often so little responsible
and circumstances are often so powerful. Our impenetrable nature is so capricious, our instincts are so
mysterious that we must be tolerant and even indul-
gent in the presence of faults which are not really
crimes, and which exhibit nothing vicious or abandoned in the man himself.

MME. DE RONCHARD

So, then, to deceive one's wife is not deceitful,
and you say such a thing before your son? Truly, a
pretty state of affairs! [*Crosses* L.]

LÉON

Oh, I have my opinion also about that, my dear Aunt.

PETITPRÉ [*rises*]

It is not almost a crime,—it is one. But it is looked upon to-day as so common a thing that one scarcely punishes it at all. It is punished by divorce, which is a house of refuge for most men. The law prefers to separate them with decency—timidly, rather than drag them apart as in former times.

MME. DE RONCHARD

Your learned theories are revolting, and I wish—

LÉON [*rises*]

Ah, here is Monsieur Martinel.

SCENE III.

(*The same, and* Monsieur Martinel.)

MARTINEL [*with great emotion*]

I come to fulfill an exceedingly difficult task. Jean, who has gone to his own house, before daring to present himself here, has sent Doctor Pellerin to me. I am commissioned by him to make you acquainted with the sad position in which Jean finds himself,— in which we all find ourselves.

MME. DE RONCHARD

Ah, ha! Now, I am going to learn something!

14   G. de M.—12

MARTINEL

By a letter which you will read presently, we
have learned this evening, in this house, of a new
misfortune. A woman of whose existence you are
all aware was at the point of death.

MME. DE RONCHARD

Did I not predict that she would do just this
thing?

LÉON

Let M. Martinel speak, my dear Aunt.

MME. DE RONCHARD

And now that this woman has seen him, how
does she feel — his dying patient? Better, without a
doubt?

MARTINEL [*quietly*]

She died, Madame, died before his eyes.

MME. DE RONCHARD

Died this evening! Impossible!

MARTINEL

Nevertheless, it is so, Madame.

LÉON [*aside*]

Poor little Musotte!

MARTINEL

There is a serious thing to be considered here.
This woman left a child, and that child's father is
Jean.

MME. DE RONCHARD [*stupefied*]

A child!

MARTINEL [*to* Petitpré]

Read the physician's letter, Monsieur. [*Hands* Petitpré *the letter, and* Petitpré *reads it.*]

MME. DE RONCHARD

He had a child and he has never confessed it; has never said anything about it; has hidden it from us! What infamy!

MARTINEL

He would have told you in due time.

MME. DE RONCHARD

He would have told! That is altogether too strong —you are mocking us!

LÉON

But, my dear Aunt, let my father answer. I shall go and find Gilberte. She will be dying of anxiety. We have no right to hide the truth from her any longer. I am going to acquaint her with it.

MME. DE RONCHARD [*accompanying him to the door*]

You have a pleasant task, but you will not succeed in arranging matters.

LÉON [*at door* L.]

In any case I shall not embroil them with each other as you would. [*Exit* L.

Scene IV.

(Petitpré, Martinel, *and* Madame de Ronchard.)

PETITPRÉ [*who has finished reading the letter*]

Then, Martinel, you say that your nephew was ignorant of the situation of this woman.

MARTINEL

Upon my honor.

MME. DE RONCHARD

It is incredible.

MARTINEL

I will answer you in a word. If my nephew had known of this situation, would he have done what he has this evening?

PETITPRÉ

Explain yourself more clearly.

MARTINEL

It is very simple. If he had known sooner of the danger this woman was in, do you think that he would have waited until the last moment, and have chosen this very evening—this supreme moment— to say good-bye to this poor, dying woman, and to reveal to you the existence of his illegitimate son? No, men hide these unfortunate children when and how they please. You know that as well as I, Monsieur. To run the risk of throwing us all into such a state of emotion and threatening his own future, as he has done, it would seem that Jean must be a madman, and he is by no means that. Had he known sooner of this situation, do you think that he would not have confided in me, and that I would have been so stupid — yes, I — as not to avert this disaster? Why, I tell you it is as clear as day.

MME. DE RONCHARD [*agitated, walks to and fro rapidly* L.]

Clear as the day — clear as the day!

MARTINEL

Yes, indeed. If we had not received this piece of news as a bomb which destroys the power of reflection, if we could have taken time to reason the thing out, to make plans, we could have hidden everything from you, and the devil would have been in it before you would have known anything! Our fault has been that of being too sincere and too loyal. Yet, I do not regret it; it is always better to act openly in life.

MME. DE RONCHARD

Permit me, Monsieur —

PETITPRÉ

Silence, Clarisse. [*To* Martinel.] Be it so, Monsieur. There is no question of your honor or of your loyalty, which have been absolutely patent in this unfortunate affair. I willingly admit that your nephew knew nothing of the situation, but how about the child? What is there to prove that it is Jean's?

MARTINEL

Jean alone can prove or disprove that. He believes it, and you know that it is not to his interest
to believe it. There is nothing very joyful about such
a complication — a poor, little foundling thrusting
himself upon one like a thunderbolt, without warning, and upon the very evening of one's marriage.
But Jean believes that the child is his, and I — and
all of us — must we not accept it as he has accepted
it, as the child's father has accepted it? Come, now.
[*A short silence.*] You ask me to prove to you that
this child belongs to Jean?

MME. DE RONCHARD AND PETITPRÉ [*together*]

Yes!

MARTINEL

Then first prove to me that it is not Jean's child.

MME. DE RONCHARD

You ask an impossibility.

MARTINEL

And so do you. The principal judge in the matter, look you, is my nephew himself. We others can
do nothing but accept his decision.

MME. DE RONCHARD

But meanwhile —

PETITPRÉ

Silence, Clarisse. Monsieur Martinel is right.

MME. DE RONCHARD [*ironically*]

Say that again.

MARTINEL

There can be no better reason, Madame. [*To* Petitpré.] I was quite sure that you would understand me, Monsieur, for you are a man of sense.

MME. DE RONCHARD

And what am I, then?

MARTINEL

You are a woman of the world, Madame.

MME. DE RONCHARD

And it is exactly as a woman of the world that I protest, Monsieur. You have a very pretty way of putting things, but none the less this is a fact: Jean Martinel brings to his bride, as a nuptial present, on the day of his marriage, an illegitimate child. Well, I ask you, woman of the world or not, can she accept such a thing?

PETITPRÉ

My sister is in the right this time, Monsieur Martinel.

MME. DE RONCHARD

And by no means too soon.

PETITPRÉ

It is evident that a situation exists patent and undeniable, which places us in an awkward dilemma. We have wedded our daughter to a man supposedly free from all ties and all complications in life, and then comes — what you know has come. The consequences should be endured by him, not by us. We have been wounded and deceived in our confidence, and the consent that we have given to this marriage we should certainly have refused, had we known the actual circumstances.

MME. DE RONCHARD

We should have refused? I should say so — not only once, but twice. Besides, this child, if Jean brings it into the house, will certainly be a cause of trouble among us all. Consider, Gilberte will probably become a mother in her turn, and then what jealousies, what rivalries, what hatred, perhaps, will arise between this intruder and her own children. This child will be a veritable apple of discord.

MARTINEL

Oh, no, no! he will not be a burden to anyone. Thanks to Jean's liberality, this child's mother will have left him enough to live comfortably, and, later, when he has become a man, he will travel, no doubt. He will do as I have done; as nine-tenths of the human race do.

PETITPRÉ

Well, until then, who will take care of it?

MARTINEL

I, if it is agreeable. I am a free man, retired from business; and it will give me something to do, something to distract me. I am ready to take him with

me at once, the poor little thing — [*looks at* Mme. de
Ronchard] unless Madame, who is so fond of saving
lost dogs —

MME. DE RONCHARD

That child! I! Oh, that *would* be a piece of foolishness.

MARTINEL

Yet, Madame, if you care to have him, I will
yield my right most willingly.

MME. DE RONCHARD

But Monsieur, I never said —

MARTINEL

Not as yet, true, but perhaps you will say it before very long, for I am beginning to understand you.
You are an assumed man-hater and nothing else. You
have been unhappy in your married life and that has
embittered you — just as milk may turn upon its surface, but at the bottom of the churn there is butter
of fine quality.

MME. DE RONCHARD [*frowns*]

What a comparison! — milk — butter — pshaw! how
vulgar!

PETITPRÉ

But Clarisse —

MARTINEL

Here is your daughter.

Scene V.

(The same, and Gilberte *and* Léon *who enter* L.*)*

PETITPRÉ [*approaches* Gilberte]

Before seeing your husband again, if you decide to see him, it is necessary that we should decide exactly what you are going to say to him.

GILBERTE [*greatly moved, sits* L. *of table*]

I knew it was some great misfortune.

MARTINEL [*sits beside her*]

Yes, my child; but there are two kinds of misfortune — those that come from the faults of men, and those that spring purely from the hazards of fate; that is to say, destiny. In the first case, the man is guilty; in the second case, he is a victim. Do you understand me?

GILBERTE

Yes, Monsieur.

MARTINEL

A misfortune of which some one person is the victim can also wound another person very cruelly. But will not the heart of this second wounded and altogether innocent person bestow a pardon upon the involuntary author of her disaster?

GILBERTE [*in a sad voice*]

That depends upon the suffering which she undergoes.

MARTINEL

Meanwhile, you knew that before Jean loved you, before he conceived the idea of marrying you, he had — an intrigue. You accepted the fact as one which had nothing exceptional about it.

GILBERTE

I did accept it.

MARTINEL

And now your brother may tell you the rest.

GILBERTE

Yes, Monsieur.

MARTINEL

What shall I say to Jean?

GILBERTE

I am too much agitated to tell you yet. This woman, of whom I did not think at all, whose very existence was a matter of indifference to me — her death has frightened me. It seems that she has come between Jean and me, and will always remain there. Everything that I have heard of her prophesies this estrangement. But you knew her — this woman — did you not, Monsieur?

MARTINEL

Yes, Madame, and I can say nothing but good of her. Your brother and I have always looked upon her as irreproachable in her fidelity to Jean. She loved him with a pure, devoted, absolute, and lasting affection. I speak as a man who has deplored deeply

this intrigue, for I look upon myself as a father to
Jean, but we must try to be just to everyone.

GILBERTE

And did Jean love her very much, too?

MARTINEL

Oh, yes, certainly he did, but his love began to
wane. Between them there was too much of a moral
and social distance. He lived with her, however,
drawn to her by the knowledge of the deep and
tender affection which she bestowed upon him.

GILBERTE [*gravely*]

And Jean went to see her die?

MARTINEL

He had just time to say farewell to her.

GILBERTE [*to herself*]

If I could only tell what passed between them at
that moment! Ah, this wretched death is worse for
me than if she were alive!

MME. DE RONCHARD [*rises R. and goes up stage*]

I really do not understand you, my dear. The
woman has died—so much the better for you. May
God deliver you from all such!

GILBERTE

No, my dear Aunt; the feeling I have just now is
so painful that I would sooner know her to be far
away than to know her dead.

PETITPRÉ [*comes down*]

Yes, I admit that is the sentiment of a woman moved by a horrible catastrophe; but there is one grave complication in the matter—that of the child. Whatever may be done with it, he will none the less be the son of my son-in-law and a menace to us all.

MME. DE RONCHARD

And a subject for ridicule. See what the world will say of us in a little while.

LÉON

Leave the world to itself, my dear Aunt, and let us occupy ourselves with our own business. [*Goes to* Gilberte.] Now, Gilberte, is it the idea of the child that moves you so deeply?

GILBERTE

Oh, no,—the poor little darling!

PETITPRÉ

Such is the foolishness of women who know nothing of life.

LÉON

Well, father, why, if we have so many different views,—according as we are spectators or actors in the course of events,—why is there so much difference between the life of the imagination and the actual life; between that which one ought to do; that which you would that others should do, and that which you do yourself. Yes, what has happened is very painful; but the surprise of the event, its coincidence with the nuptial day makes it still more painful. We magnify everything in our emotion, when it is ourselves that misfortune touches. Suppose, for a moment, that you had read this in your daily newspaper—

MME. DE RONCHARD [*seated* L. *of table, indignantly*]

In my daily newspaper!

LÉON

Or in a romance. What emotion we should feel; what tears we should shed! How your sympathy would quickly go out to the poor little child whose birth was attained at the cost of his mother's life! How Jean would go up in your esteem; how frank, how loyal, how stanch in his fealty you would consider him; while, on the other hand, if he had deserted the dying woman, and had spirited away the little one into some distant village, you would not have had enough scorn for him, or enough insults for him. You would look upon him as a being without heart and without fear; and, you, my dear Aunt, thinking of the innumerable little bad dogs who owe you their lives, you would cry out with forcible gestures: "What a miserable scoundrel!"

MARTINEL [*seated* L.]

That's perfectly true.

MME. DE RONCHARD

Dogs are worth more than men.

LÉON

Little children are not men, my dear Aunt. They have not had time to become bad.

PETITPRÉ

All that is very ingenious, Léon, and your special pleading is magnificent.

MME. DE RONCHARD

Yes, if you would only plead like that at the Palais.

PETITPRÉ

But this has nothing to do with a romance or with imaginary personages. We have married Gilberte to a young man in the ordinary conditions of life.

MME. DE RONCHARD

Without enthusiasm.

PETITPRÉ

Without enthusiasm, it is true, but nevertheless they are married, just the same. Now, on the evening of his nuptials, he brings us a present — I must say I do not care for a present which bawls.

LÉON

What does that prove, unless it is that your son-in-law is a brave man? What he has just done — risked his happiness in order to accomplish his duty — does it not say better than anything else could, how capable of devotion he is?

MARTINEL

Clear as the day.

MME. DE RONCHARD [*aside*]

And this man from Havre admires him!

PETITPRÉ

Then you maintain that Gilberte, on the day of her entry upon married life, should become the adopted mother of the son of her husband's mistress?

LÉON

Exactly; just as I maintain all that is honorable and disinterested. And you would think as I do if the thing did not concern your daughter.

PETITPRÉ

No; it is an inexcusable situation.

LÉON

Well, then, what do you propose to do?

PETITPRÉ

Well, nothing less than a divorce. The scandal of this night is sufficient.

MME. DE RONCHARD [*rises*]

Gilberte divorced! You don't dream of that, do you? Have all our friends closing their doors on her, —the greater part of her relatives lost to her! Divorced! Come, come! in spite of your new law, that has not yet come into our custom and shall not come in so soon. Religion forbids it; the world accepts it only under protest; and when you have against you both religion and the world —

But statistics prove —

Pshaw! Statistics! You can make them say what you wish. No, no divorce for Gilberte. [*In a soft, low voice.*] Simply a legal separation — that is admissible, at least, and it is good form. Let them separate. I am separated — all fashionable people separate, and everything goes all right, but as to divorce —

It seems to me that only one person has a right to speak in this matter, and we are forgetting her too long. [*Turns to* Gilberte.] You have heard everything, Gilberte; you are mistress of your own judgment and of your decision. Upon a word from you depend either pardon or rupture. My father has made his argument. What does your heart say? [Gilberte *tries to speak, but stops and breaks down.*] Think always that in refusing to pardon Jean you wound me, and if I see you unhappy from your determination to say no, I shall suffer exceedingly. Monsieur Martinel asks from you at once an answer for Jean. Let us do better. I will go and find him. It is from your lips; it is, above all, in your eyes, that he will learn his fate. [*Brings her gently to the front of the stage.*] My little sister, my dear little sister, don't be too proud; don't be too haughty! Listen to that

14 G. de M.—13

which your chagrin murmurs in your soul. Listen well, but do not mistake it for pride.

GILBERTE

But I have no pride. I do not know how I feel. I am ill. My joy has been blighted, and it poisons me.

LÉON

Take care! It takes so little in such moments as these to make wounds which are incurable.

GILBERTE

No, no! I am too much distressed. Perhaps I shall be hard, for I am afraid of him and of myself. I am afraid of breaking off everything, or of yielding everything.

LÉON

I am going to find Jean.

GILBERTE [*resolutely*]

No, I do not wish to see him. I forbid it!

LÉON

Let me tell you something, my little Gilberte: You are less intelligent than I thought.

GILBERTE

Why?

LÉON

Because in such moments as these it is necessary to say yes or no at once. [Jean *appears at door* R.]

SCENE VI.

(The same, and Jean Martinel *standing at door* R.)

GILBERTE [*with a stifled cry*]

It is he!

LÉON [*goes up to* Jean *and taking him by the hand*]

Welcome!

JEAN

I am like a prisoner awaiting the decision of his judges — whether it be acquittal or death. The moments through which I have just passed I shall never forget.

LÉON

Your uncle and I have said all that we had to say. Now speak for yourself.

JEAN

I do not know how. It must be to my wife alone. I dare not speak before you all. I ask but a moment. After that I go, and I shall leave the house if my wife's attitude indicates that I ought. I shall do exactly what she would have me. I shall become that which she may order. But I must hear from her *own* lips her decision as to my life. [*To* Gilberte.] You cannot refuse me that, Madame. It is the only prayer that I shall ever make to you, I swear, if this request to you remains ungranted. [*They stand face to face and look at each other.*]

GILBERTE

No, I cannot refuse you. Father, Aunt, please leave me alone for a few minutes with Monsieur Martinel. You can see that I am perfectly calm.

PETITPRÉ

But — but —

JEAN [*determinedly to* M. Petitpré]

Monsieur, I shall not gainsay your will in anything. I shall do nothing without your approval. I have not returned here to contest your authority or to speak of rights; but I respectfully ask permission to remain alone a few minutes with — my wife! Consider that this is perhaps our last interview and that our future depends upon it.

MME. DE RONCHARD

It is solely the future of Gilberte which concerns me.

JEAN [*to* Mme. de Ronchard]

I appeal simply to your heart, Madame; your heart, which has suffered. Do not forget that your irritation and your bitterness against me come from the misfortune that another man has inflicted upon you. Your life has been broken by him. Do not wish the same for me. You have been unhappy; married scarcely a year. [*Points to* Gilberte.] Will you say that she shall be married scarcely a day, and that later she shall talk of her broken life — ceaselessly guarding in her mind the memory of this evening's disaster? [*At a movement of* Mme. de Ronchard.]

I know you to be kind, although you deny it, and I promise you, Madame, that if I remain Gilberte's husband, I shall love you as a son, as a son worthy of you.

MME. DE RONCHARD [*very much moved*]

A son! He has stirred me deeply! [*Whispers to* Petitpré.] Come away, let us leave them alone. [*Embraces* Gilberte.]

PETITPRÉ [*to* Jean]

Well, so be it, Monsieur. [*Rises and exit* C., *offering his arm to* Mme. de Ronchard.]

MARTINEL [*to* Léon]

They are going to talk with that [*touches his heart*]; it is the only true eloquence.

[*Exit with* Léon C.

SCENE VII.

(Gilberte *and* Jean.)

JEAN

You know all, do you not?

GILBERTE

Yes. And I have been deeply wounded.

JEAN

I hope you do not accuse me of lying or of any other dissimulation.

GILBERTE

Oh, no!

JEAN

Do you blame me for having left you this evening?

GILBERTE

I blame no one who does his duty.

JEAN

You did not know this woman — and she is dead.

GILBERTE

It is just because she is dead that she troubles me thus.

JEAN

Impossible; you must have another reason. [*With hesitation.*] The child?

GILBERTE [*quickly*]

No, no! don't deceive yourself. The poor little darling! it is not his fault. No, I suffer from something which is peculiar to myself, which can come only from me, and which I cannot confess to you. It is a sorrow deep in my heart, so keen, when I felt it spring to birth under the words of my brother and your uncle, that, should I ever experience it again when living with you as your wife, I should never be able to dispel it.

JEAN

What is it?

GILBERTE

I cannot tell it. [*Sits* L.]

JEAN [*stands*]

Listen to me. It is necessary that at this moment there should not be between us the shadow of a misunderstanding. All our life depends upon it. You are my wife, but I admit that you are absolutely free after what has happened. I will do as you wish. I am ready to agree to everything you desire, even to a divorce if you demand it. But what will happen to me after that I do not know, for I love you so that the thought of losing you after winning you will throw me mercilessly into some desperate resolve. [*Sees* Gilberte *moved.*] I do not seek to soften you, to move you — I simply tell you the naked truth. I feel, and I have felt during the whole night, through all the shocks and horrible emotions of the drama that has just been enacted, that you hold for me the keenest wound. If you banish me now, I am a lost man.

GILBERTE [*much moved*]

Do you really love me as much as that?

JEAN

With a love that I feel is ineffaceable.

GILBERTE

Did you love her?

JEAN

I did indeed love her. I experienced a tender attachment for a gentle and devoted girl. [*In a low voice,*

with passion.]   Listen: that which I am going to
tell you is unworthy, perhaps infamous, but I am
only a human being, feeble as anyone else. Well,
just now, in the presence of this poor, dying girl,
my eyes were filled with tears and my sobs choked
me — all my being vibrated with sorrow; but at the
bottom of my soul, in the depths of my being, I
thought only of you.

GILBERTE [*rises quickly*]

Do you mean that?

JEAN [*simply*]

I cannot lie to you.

GILBERTE

Well, do you know what made me suffer just
now when my brother told me of this intrigue and
death? I can tell it to you now. I was jealous! It
was unworthy of me, wasn't it? Jealous of this poor,
dead woman! But he spoke so well of her as to
move me, and I felt that she loved you so much that
you might find me perhaps indifferent and cold after
her, and that hurt me so! I had so much fear of ex-
periencing that that I thought of renouncing you.

JEAN

And now? — Gilberte! Gilberte!

GILBERTE [*extends her hands*]

I am here, Jean! take me!

JEAN

Ah, how grateful I am. [*Kisses her hands; then immediately after, with emotion.*] But here another anguish seizes me. I have promised this poor woman to take and cherish this child in my own home. [Gilberte *makes a movement.*] That is not all. Do you know what her last thought, her last prayer was? She entreated me to commend the child to you.

GILBERTE

To me!

JEAN

To you, Gilberte.

GILBERTE [*profoundly moved*]

She did this, the poor woman? Did she believe that I would take —

JEAN

She hoped it, and in that hope her death was made easier.

GILBERTE [*in exalted mood, crosses* R.]

Yes, I will take it! where is it?

JEAN

At my house.

GILBERTE

At your house? You must go to it immediately.

JEAN

What! leave you now, at this moment?

GILBERTE

We will go together, since I was to have accompanied you to your house this evening.

JEAN [*joyously*]

Oh, Gilberte! But your father will not let us go.

GILBERTE

Well, do you know what we must do, since my packing is finished, and my maid awaits me at your house? You must carry me off.

JEAN

Carry you off?

GILBERTE

Give me my cloak and let us go. All can be explained to-morrow. [*Shows the cloak that she had left upon the chair in the first act.*] My cloak, please.

JEAN [*picks up the cloak quickly and throws it over her shoulders*]

You are the most adorable creature! [Gilberte *takes his arm and they go toward door* R.]

SCENE VIII.

(*Enter* Mme. de Ronchard, M. Petitpré, M. Martinel, *and* Léon C.)

MME. DE RONCHARD

Well, what are they doing? Are they going away now?

PETITPRÉ

Why, what does it mean?

GILBERTE

Yes; father, I am going away. I am going with my husband; but I shall be here to-morrow to ask pardon for this hurried flight, and to explain to you the reason for it.

PETITPRÉ

Were you going without saying good-bye to us — without embracing us?

GILBERTE

Yes, in order to avoid more discussions.

LÉON

She is right. Let them go.

GILBERTE [*throws herself upon* Petitpré's *neck*]

Till to-morrow, father; till to-morrow, my dear Aunt. Good night, all; I have had enough of emotion and fatigue.

MME. DE RONCHARD [*goes to* Gilberte *and embraces her*]

Yes, run along, darling—there is a little one over there who waits for a mother!

Curtain.

THE LANCER'S WIFE
AND
OTHER TALES

THE LANCER'S WIFE

IT WAS after Bourbaki's defeat in the east of France. The army, broken up, decimated and worn out, had been obliged to retreat into Switzerland, after that terrible campaign. It was only the short duration of the struggle that saved a hundred and fifty thousand men from certain death. Hunger, the terrible cold, and forced marches in the snow without boots, over bad mountainous roads, had caused the *francs-tireurs* especially the greatest suffering, for we were without tents and almost without food, always in front when we were marching toward Belfort, and in the rear when returning by the Jura. Of our brigade, that had numbered twelve hundred men on the first of January, there remained only twenty-two pale, thin, ragged wretches, when at length we succeeded in reaching Swiss territory.

There we were safe and could rest. Everybody knows what sympathy was shown to the unfortunate French army, and how well it was cared for. We all gained fresh life, and those who had been rich and happy before the war declared that they had never experienced a greater feeling of comfort than they did then. Just think. We actually had something to eat every day, and could sleep every night.

Meanwhile, the war continued in the east of France, which had been excluded from the armistice. Besançon still kept the enemy in check, and the latter had their revenge by ravaging the Comte Franché. Sometimes we heard that they had approached quite close to the frontier, and we saw Swiss troops, who were to form a line of observation between us and the Germans, set out on their march.

But this hurt our pride, and as we regained health and strength the longing for fighting laid hold of us. It was disgraceful and irritating to know that within two or three leagues of us the Germans were victorious and insolent, to feel that we were protected by our captivity, and to feel that on that account we were powerless against them.

One day, our captain took five or six of us aside, and spoke to us about it, long and earnestly. He was a fine fellow, that captain. He had been a sub-lieutenant in the Zouaves, was tall and thin and as hard as steel, and during the whole campaign had given a great deal of trouble to the Germans. He fretted in inactivity and could not accustom himself to the idea of being a prisoner and of doing nothing.

"Confound it!" he said to us, "does it not pain you to know that there are a lot of uhlans within two hours of us? Does it not almost drive you mad to know that those beggarly wretches are walking about as masters in our mountains, where six determined men might kill a whole troop any day? I cannot endure it any longer, and I must go there."

"But how can you manage it, Captain?"

"How? It is not very difficult! Just as if we had not done a thing or two within the last six months, and got out of woods that were guarded by men very different from the Swiss. The day that you wish to cross over into France, I will undertake to get you there."

"That may be; but what shall we do in France without any arms?"

" Without arms? We will get them over yonder, by Jove!"

"You are forgetting the treaty," another soldier said; "we shall run the risk of doing the Swiss an injury, if Manteuffel learns that they have allowed prisoners to return to France."

"Come," said the captain, "those are all poor reasons. I mean to go and kill some Prussians; that is all I care about. If you do not wish to do as I do, well and good; only say so at once. I can quite well go by myself; I do not require anybody's company."

Naturally we all protested, and as it was quite impossible to make the captain alter his mind, we felt obliged to promise to go with him. We liked him too much to leave him in the lurch, since he had never failed us in any extremity; and so the expedition was decided on.

II.

The captain had a plan of his own, a plan he had been cogitating over for some time. A man in that part of the country, whom he knew, was going to lend him a cart, and six suits of peasants' clothes. We could hide under some straw at the bottom of the wagon, which would be loaded with Gruyère cheese. This cheese he was supposed to be going to sell in France. The captain told the sentinels that he was taking two friends with him to protect his goods, in case anyone should try to rob him, which did not seem an extraordinary precaution. A Swiss officer seemed to look at the wagon in a knowing manner, but that was in order to impress his soldiers. In a word, neither officers nor men made it out.

"Get on," the captain said to the horses, as he cracked his whip, while our men quietly smoked their pipes. I was half suffocated in my box, which only admitted the air through some holes in front, while at the same time I was nearly frozen, for it was terribly cold.

"Get on," the captain said again, and the wagon loaded with Gruyère cheese entered France.

The Prussian lines were very badly guarded, as the enemy trusted to the watchfulness of the Swiss. The sergeant spoke North German, while our captain spoke the bad German of the "Four Cantons"; so they could not understand each other. The sergeant, however, pretended to be very intelligent, and in order to make us believe that he understood us, they allowed us to continue our journey, and after traveling for seven hours, being continually stopped in the same manner, we arrived at a small village of the Jura, in ruins, at nightfall.

What were we going to do? Our only arms were the captain's whip, our uniforms, the peasants' blouses, and our food the Gruyère cheese. Our sole riches consisted in our ammunition, packets of cartridges which we had stowed away inside some of the huge cheeses. We had about a thousand of them, just two hundred each; but then we wanted rifles, and they must be *chassepots;* luckily, however, the captain was a bold man of an inventive mind, and this was the plan that he hit upon:

While three of us remained hidden in a cellar in the abandoned village, he continued his journey as far as Besançon with the empty wagon and one man. The town was invested, but one can always make one's way into a town among the hills by crossing the table-land till within about ten miles of the walls, and then by following paths and ravines on foot. They left their wagon at Omans, among the Germans, and escaped out of it at night on foot, so as to gain the heights which border the river Doubs; the next day they entered Besançon, where there were plenty of *chassepots*. There were nearly forty thousand of them left in the arsenal, and General Roland, a brave marine, laughed at the captain's daring project, but let him have six rifles and wished him "good luck." There he also found his wife, who had been through all the war with us before the campaign in the east, and who had been only prevented by illness from continuing with Bourbaki's army. She had recovered, however, in spite of the cold, which was growing more and more intense, and in spite of the numberless privations that awaited her, she insisted on accompanying her husband. He was obliged to give way to her, and all three, the captain, his wife, and our comrade, started on their expedition.

Going was nothing in comparison to returning.
They were obliged to travel by night, so as to avoid
meeting anybody, as the possession of six rifles
would have made them liable to suspicion. But in
spite of everything, a week after leaving us, the captain and his "two men" were back with us again.
The campaign was about to begin.

III.

The first night of his arrival, the captain began it
himself. Under the pretext of examining the country
round, he went along the highroad. I must tell you
that the little village which served as our fortress was
a small collection of poor, badly built houses, which
had been deserted long before. It lay on a steep
slope, which terminated in a wooded plain. The
country people sold wood; they sent it down the
ravines, which are called *coulées* locally, and which
led down to the plain, and there they stacked it into
piles, which were sold thrice a year to the wood
merchants. The spot where this market was held was
indicated by two small houses by the side of the
highroad, which served for public-houses. The captain had gone down there by one of these *coulées*.

He had been gone about half an hour, and we
were on the lookout at the top of the ravine, when
we heard a shot. The captain had ordered us not to
stir, and only to come to him when we heard him
blow his trumpet. It was made of a goat's horn,
and could be heard a league off, but it gave no
sound, and in spite of our cruel anxiety, we were

obliged to wait in silence, with our rifles by our side.

To go down these *coulées* is easy, you need only let yourself glide down; but it is more difficult to get up again. You have to scramble up by catching hold of the hanging branches of the trees, and sometimes on all fours, by sheer strength. A whole mortal hour passed, and still the captain did not come, nothing moved in the brushwood. The captain's wife began to grow impatient; what could he be doing? Why did he not call us? Did the shot that we had heard proceed from an enemy, and had he killed or wounded our leader, her husband? They did not know what to think, but I myself fancied that either he was dead or that his enterprise was successful. I was merely anxious and curious to know which.

Suddenly, we heard the sound of his trumpet, and were much surprised that instead of coming from below, as we had expected, it came from the village behind us. What did that mean? It was a mystery to us, but the same idea struck us all, that he had been killed, and that the Prussians were blowing the trumpet to draw us into an ambush. We therefore returned to the cottage, keeping a careful lookout, with our fingers on the trigger and hiding under the branches. But his wife, in spite of our entreaties, rushed on, leaping like a tigress. She thought that she had to avenge her husband, and had fixed the bayonet to her rifle. We lost sight of her at the moment that we heard the trumpet again, and a few moments later we heard her calling out to us:

"Come on! come on! he is alive! it is he!"

We hastened on, and saw the captain smoking his pipe at the entrance of the village, but strangely enough he was on horseback.

"Ah!" said he to us, "you see that there is something to be done here. Here I am on horseback already; I knocked over a uhlan yonder, and took his horse; I suppose they were guarding the wood, but it was by drinking and swilling in clover. One of them, the sentry at the door, had not time to see me before I gave him a sugarplum in his stomach, and then, before the others could come out, I jumped on to the horse and was off like a shot. Eight or ten of them followed me, I think, but I took the crossroads through the wood; I have got scratched and torn a bit, but here I am. And now, my good fellows, attention, and take care! Those brigands will not rest until they have caught us, and we must receive them with rifle bullets. Come along; let us take up our posts!"

We set out. One of us took up his position a good way from the village of the crossroads; I was posted at the entrance of the main street, where the road from the level country enters the village, while the two others, with the captain and his wife, took up positions in the middle of the village, near the church, whose tower served for an observatory and citadel.

We had not been in our places long before we heard a shot followed by another; then two, then three. The first was evidently a *chassepot,*—one recognized it by the sharp report, which sounds like the crack of a whip,—while the other three came from the lancers' carbines.

The captain was furious. He had given orders to the outpost to let the enemy pass, and merely to follow them at a distance if they marched toward the village, and to join me when they had gone well between the houses. Then they were to appear suddenly, take the patrol between two fires, and not allow a single man to escape, for posted as we were, the six of us could have hemmed in ten Prussians, if needful.

"That confounded Piédelot has roused them," the captain said, "and they will not venture to come on blindfold any longer. And then I am quite sure that he has managed to get wounded himself somehow or other, for we hear nothing of him. It serves him right; why did he not obey orders?" And then, after a moment, he grumbled in his beard: "After all, I am sorry for the poor fellow; he is so brave and shoots so well!"

The captain was right in his conjectures. We waited until evening, without seeing the uhlans; they had retreated after the first attack, but unfortunately we had not seen Piédelot either. Was he dead or a prisoner? When night came the captain proposed that we should go out and look for him, and so the three of us started. At the crossroads we found a broken rifle and some blood, while the ground was trampled down. But we did not find either a wounded man or a dead body, although we searched every thicket. At midnight we returned without having discovered anything of our unfortunate comrade.

"It is very strange," the captain growled. "They must have killed him and thrown him into the

bushes somewhere; they cannot possibly have taken
him prisoner, as he would have called out for help.
I cannot understand it all." Just as he said that,
bright, red flames shot up in the direction of the inn
on the highroad, which illuminated the sky.

"Scoundrels! cowards!" shouted the captain. "I
will bet that they have set fire to the two houses in
the market-place, in order to have their revenge, and
then they will scuttle off without saying a word.
They will be satisfied with having killed a man and
setting fire to two houses. All right. It shall not
pass over like that. We must go for them; they
will not like to leave their illuminations in order to
fight."

"It would be a great stroke of luck if we could
set Piédelot free at the same time," said some one.

The five of us set off, full of rage and hope. In
twenty minutes we had got to the bottom of the
couleé, and had not yet seen anyone when within a
hundred yards of the inn. The fire was behind the
house, and so all that we saw of it was the reflection above the roof. However, we were walking
rather slowly, as we were afraid of a trap, when
suddenly we heard Piédelot's well-known voice. It
had a strange sound, however, for it was at the same
time dull and vibrant, stifled and clear, as if he
was calling out as loud as he could with a gag in
his mouth. He seemed to be hoarse and panting,
and the unlucky fellow kept exclaiming: "Help!
Help!"

We sent all thoughts of prudence to the devil and
in two bounds were at the back of the inn, where a
terrible sight met our eyes.

IV.

Piédelot was being burned alive. He was writhing in the middle of a heap of fagots, against a stake to which they had fastened him, and the flames were licking him with their sharp tongues. When he saw us, his tongue seemed to stick in his throat, he drooped his head, and seemed as if he were going to die. It was only the affair of a moment to upset the burning pile, to scatter the embers, and to cut the ropes that fastened him.

Poor fellow! In what a terrible state we found him. The evening before he had had his left arm broken, and it seemed as if he had been badly beaten since then, for his whole body was covered with wounds, bruises, and blood. The flames had also begun their work on him, and he had two large burns, one on his loins, and the other on his right thigh, and his beard and his hair were scorched. Poor Piédelot!

Nobody knows the terrible rage we felt at this sight! We would have rushed headlong at a hundred thousand Prussians. Our thirst for vengeance was intense; but the cowards had run away, leaving their crime behind them. Where could we find them now? Meanwhile, however, the captain's wife was looking after Piédelot, and dressing his wounds as best she could, while the captain himself shook hands with him excitedly. In a few minutes he came to himself.

"Good morning, Captain, good morning, all of you," he said. "Ah! the scoundrels, the wretches! Why, twenty of them came to surprise us."

"Twenty, do you say?"

"Yes, there was a whole band of them, and that is why I disobeyed orders, Captain, and fired on them, for they would have killed you all. So I preferred to stop them. That frightened them, and they did not venture to go further than the crossroads. They were such cowards. Four of them shot at me at twenty yards, as if I had been a target, and then they slashed me with their swords. My arm was broken, so that I could only use my bayonet with one hand."

"But why did you not call for help?"

"I took good care not to do that, for you would all have come, and you would neither have been able to defend me nor yourselves, being only five against twenty."

"You know that we should not have allowed you to have been taken, poor old fellow."

"I preferred to die by myself, don't you see! I did not want to bring you there, for it would have been a mere ambush."

"Well, we will not talk about it any more. Do you feel rather easier?"

"No, I am suffocating. I know that I cannot live much longer. The brutes! They tied me to a tree, and beat me till I was half dead, and then they shook my broken arm, but I did not make a sound. I would rather have bitten my tongue out than have called out before them. Now I can say what I am suffering and shed tears; it does one good. Thank you, my kind friends."

"Poor Piédelot! But we will avenge you, you may be sure!"

"Yes, yes, I want you to do that. Especially, there is a woman among them, who passes as the wife of the lancer whom the captain killed yesterday. She is dressed like a lancer, and it was she who tortured me the most yesterday, and suggested burning me. In fact it was she who set fire to the wood. Oh! the wretch, the brute—Ah! how I am suffering! My loins, my arms!" and he fell back panting and exhausted, writhing in his terrible agony, while the captain's wife wiped the perspiration from his forehead. We all shed tears of grief and rage, as if we had been children. I will not describe the end to you; he died half an hour later, but before that he told us in which direction the enemy had gone. When he was dead, we gave ourselves time to bury him, and then we set out in pursuit of them, with our hearts full of fury and hatred.

"We will throw ourselves on the whole Prussian army, if it be needful," the captain said, "but we will avenge Piédelot. We must catch those scoundrels. Let us swear to die, rather than not to find them, and if I am killed first, these are my orders: all the prisoners that you make are to be shot immediately, and as for the lancer's wife, she is to be violated before she is put to death."

"She must not be shot, because she is a woman," the captain's wife said. "If you survive, I am sure that you would not shoot a woman. Outraging her will be quite sufficient. But if you are killed in this pursuit, I want one thing, and that is to fight with her; I will kill her with my own hands, and the others can do what they like with her if she kills me."

"We will outrage her! We will burn her! We will tear her to pieces! Piédelot shall be avenged, an eye for an eye, a tooth for a tooth!"

V.

The next morning we unexpectedly fell on an outpost of uhlans four leagues away. Surprised by our sudden attack, they were not able to mount their horses, nor even to defend themselves, and in a few moments we had five prisoners, corresponding to our own number. The captain questioned them, and from their answers we felt certain that they were the same whom we had encountered the previous day. Then a very curious operation took place. One of us was told off to ascertain their sex, and nothing can depict our joy when we discovered what we were seeking among them, the female executioner who had tortured our friend.

The four others were shot on the spot, with their backs toward us and close to the muzzles of our rifles, and then we turned our attention to the woman. What were we going to do with her? I must acknowledge that we were all of us in favor of shooting her. Hatred, and the wish to avenge Piédelot had extinguished all pity in us, and we had forgotten that we were going to shoot a woman. But a woman reminded us of it, the captain's wife; at her entreaties, therefore, we determined to keep her a prisoner. The captain's poor wife was to be severely punished for this act of clemency.

The next day we heard that the armistice had

been extended to the eastern part of France, and we
had to put an end to our little campaign. Two of
us, who belonged to the neighborhood, returned
home. So there remained only four of us, all told: the
captain, his wife, and two men. We belonged to
Besançon, which was still being besieged in spite of
the armistice.

"Let us stop here," said the captain. "I cannot
believe that the war is going to end like this. The
devil take it! Surely there are men still left in France,
and now is the time to prove what they are made of.
The spring is coming on, and the armistice is only a
trap laid for the Prussians. During the time that it
lasts, a new army will be formed, and some fine
morning we shall fall upon them again. We shall be
ready, and we have a hostage—let us remain here."

We fixed our quarters there. It was terribly cold,
and we did not go out much, as somebody had always to keep the female prisoner in sight.

She was sullen and never spoke save to refer to
her husband, whom the captain had killed. She
looked at him continually with fierce eyes, and we
felt that she was tortured by a wild longing for revenge. That seemed to us to be the most suitable
punishment for the terrible torments that she had
made Piédelot suffer, for impotent vengeance is such
intense pain!

Alas! we who knew how to avenge our comrade
ought to have known that this woman would find a
way to avenge her husband, and should have been
on our guard. It is true that one of us kept watch
every night, and that at first we tied her by a long
rope to the great oak bench that was fastened to the

wall. But, by and by, as she had never tried to escape, in spite of her hatred for us, we relaxed our extreme prudence and allowed her to sleep somewhere else, and without being tied. What had we to fear? She was at the end of the room, a man was on guard at the door, and between her and the sentinel the captain's wife and two other men used to lie. She was alone and unarmed against four, so there could be no danger.

One night when we were asleep, and the captain was on guard, the lancer's wife was lying more quietly in her corner than usual. She had even smiled during the evening for the first time since she had been our prisoner. Suddenly, however, in the middle of the night, we were awakened by a terrible cry. We got up, groping about. Scarcely were we up when we stumbled over a furious couple who were rolling about and fighting on the ground. It was the captain and the lancer's wife. We threw ourselves on to them and separated them in a moment. She was shouting and laughing, and he seemed to have the death rattle. All this took place in the dark. Two of us held her, and when a light was struck, a terrible sight met our eyes. The captain was lying on the floor in a pool of blood, with an enormous wound in his throat, and his sword bayonet, that had been taken from his rifle, was sticking in the red, gaping wound. A few minutes afterward he died, without having been able to utter a word.

His wife did not shed a tear. Her eyes were dry, her throat was contracted, and she looked at the lancer's wife steadfastly, and with a calm ferocity that inspired fear.

"This woman belongs to me," she said to us suddenly. "You swore to me not a week ago to let me kill her as I chose if she killed my husband, and you must keep your oath. You must fasten her securely to the fireplace, upright against the back of it, and then you can go where you like, but far from here. I will take my revenge on her to myself. Leave the captain's body, and we three, he, she, and I, will remain here."

We obeyed and went away. She promised to write to us to Geneva, as we were returning there.

VI.

Two days later, I received the following letter, dated the day after we had left. It had been written at an inn on the highroad:

"MY FRIEND:

"I am writing to you, according to my promise. For the moment I am at this inn, where I have just handed my prisoner over to a Prussian officer.

"I must tell you, my friend, that this poor woman left two children in Germany. She had followed her husband, whom she adored, as she did not wish him to be exposed to the risks of war by himself, and as her children were with their grandparents. I have learned all this since yesterday, and it has turned my ideas of vengeance into more humane feelings. At the very moment when I felt pleasure in insulting this woman, and in threatening her with the most fearful torments — in recalling Piédelot, who had been burned alive, and in threatening her with a similar death, she looked at me coldly, and said:

"'Why should you reproach me, Frenchwoman? You think that you will do right in avenging your husband's death, is not that so?'

"'Yes,' I replied.

" 'Very well then; in killing him, I did what you are going to do in burning me. I avenged my husband, for your husband killed him.'

" 'Well,' I replied, 'as you approve of this vengeance, prepare to endure it.'

" 'I do not fear it.'

"And in fact she did not seem to have lost courage. Her face was calm, and she looked at me without trembling, while I brought wood and dried leaves together, and feverishly threw on to them the powder from some cartridges, to make her funeral pile the more cruel.

"I hesitated in my thoughts of persecution for a moment. But the captain's body was there, pale and covered with blood, and he seemed to be looking at me with large, glassy eyes, and I applied myself to my work again after kissing his pale lips. Suddenly, however, on raising my head, I saw that she was crying, and I felt rather surprised.

" 'So you are frightened?' I said to her.

" 'No, but when I saw you kiss your husband, I thought of mine, of all whom I love.'

"She continued to sob, but stopping suddenly she said to me in broken words, and in a low voice:

" 'Have you any children?'

"A shiver ran over me, for I guessed that this poor woman had some. She asked me to look in a pocketbook which was in her bosom, and in it I saw two photographs of quite young children, a boy and a girl, with those kind, gentle, chubby faces that German children have. In it there were also two locks of light hair and a letter in a large childish hand, beginning with German words which meant: 'My dear little mother.'

"I could not restrain my tears, my dear friend, and so I untied her, and without venturing to look at the face of my poor, dead husband, who was not to be avenged, I went with her as far as the inn. She is free; I have just left her, and she kissed me with tears. I am going upstairs to my husband; come as soon as possible, my dear friend, to look for our two bodies."

I set off with all speed, and when I arrived there was a Prussian patrol at the cottage. When I asked what it all meant, I was told that there was a captain of *francs-tireurs* and his wife inside, both dead. I gave their names; they saw that I knew them, and I begged to be allowed to undertake their funeral.

"Somebody has already undertaken it," was the reply. "Go in if you wish to, as you knew them. You can settle about their funeral with their friend."

I went in. The captain and his wife were lying side by side on a bed, and were covered by a sheet. I raised it, and saw that the woman had inflicted a wound in her throat similar to that from which her husband had died.

At the side of the bed there sat, watching and weeping, the woman who had been mentioned to me as their last friend. It was the lancer's wife.

14   G. de M.—15

HAUTOT SENIOR AND
HAUTOT JUNIOR

I.

IN FRONT of the building, half farmhouse, half manor-house, one of those rural habitations of a mixed character which were all but seigneurial, and which are at the present time occupied by large cultivators, the dogs, lashed beside the apple-trees in the orchard near the house, kept barking and howling at the sight of the shooting-bags carried by the gamekeepers and the boys. In the spacious dining-room kitchen, Hautot Senior and Hautot Junior, M. Bermont, the tax-collector, and M. Mondaru, the notary, were taking a bite and drinking some wine before going out to shoot, for it was the opening day.

Hautot Senior, proud of all his possessions, talked boastfully beforehand of the game which his guests were going to find on his lands. He was a big Norman, one of those powerful, ruddy, bony men, who can lift wagonloads of apples on their shoulders. Half peasant, half gentleman, rich, respected, influential, invested with authority, he made his son

César go as far as the third form at school, so that he might be an educated man, and there he had brought his studies to a stop for fear of his becoming a fine gentleman and paying no attention to the land.

César Hautot, almost as tall as his father, but thinner, was a good son, docile, content with everything, full of admiration, respect, and deference for the wishes and opinions of his sire.

M. Bermont, the tax-collector, a stout little man, who showed on his red cheeks a thin network of violet veins resembling the tributaries and the winding courses of rivers on maps, asked:

"And hares — are there any hares on it?"

Hautot Senior answered:

"As many as you like, especially in the Puysatier lands."

"Which direction shall we begin in?" asked the notary, a jolly notary, fat and pale, big-paunched too, and strapped up in an entirely new hunting costume bought at Rouen.

"Well, that way, through these grounds. We will drive the partridges into the plain, and we will beat there again."

And Hautot Senior rose up. They all followed his example, took their guns out of the corners, examined the locks, stamped with their feet in order to feel themselves firmer in their boots which were rather hard, not having as yet been rendered flexible by the heat of the blood. Then they went out; and the dogs, standing erect at the ends of their leashes, gave vent to piercing howls while beating the air with their paws.

They set forth for the lands referred to. These consisted of a little glen, or rather a long undulating stretch of inferior soil, which had on that account remained uncultivated, furrowed with mountain-torrents, covered with ferns, an excellent preserve for game.

The sportsmen took up their positions at some distance from each other, Hautot Senior posting himself at the right, Hautot Junior at the left, and the two guests in the middle. The keeper and those who carried the game-bags followed. It was the anxious moment when the first shot is awaited, when the heart beats a little, while the nervous finger keeps feeling at the trigger every second.

Suddenly the shot went off. Hautot Senior had fired. They all stopped, and saw a partridge breaking off from a covey which was rushing along at great speed to fall down into a ravine under a thick growth of brushwood. The sportsman, becoming excited, rushed forward with rapid strides, thrusting aside the briers which stood in his path, and disappeared in his turn into the thicket in quest of his game.

Almost at the same instant, a second shot was heard.

"Ha! ha! the rascal!" exclaimed M. Bermont, "he will unearth a hare down there."

They all waited, with their eyes riveted on the heap of branches through which their gaze failed to penetrate.

The notary, making a speaking-trumpet of his hands, shouted:

"Have you got them?"

Hautot Senior made no response.

Then César, turning toward the keeper, said to him:

"Just go and assist him, Joseph. We must keep walking in a straight line. We'll wait."

And Joseph, an old stump of a man, lean and knotty, all of whose joints formed protuberances, proceeded at an easy pace down the ravine, searching at every opening through which a passage could be effected with the cautiousness of a fox. Then, suddenly, he cried:

"Oh! come! come! an unfortunate thing has occurred."

They all hurried forward, plunging through the briers.

The elder Hautot, who had fallen on his side, in a fainting condition, kept both his hands over his stomach, from which flowed down upon the grass through the linen vest torn by the lead, long streamlets of blood. As he was laying down his gun, in order to seize the partridge within reach of him, he had let the firearm fall, and the second discharge, going off with the shock, had torn open his entrails. They drew him out of the trench; they removed his clothes and they saw a frightful wound, through which the intestines came out. Then, after having bandaged him the best way they could, they brought him back to his own house, and awaited the doctor, who had been sent for, as well as a priest.

When the doctor arrived, he gravely shook his head, and, turning toward young Hautot, who was sobbing on a chair:

"My poor boy," said he, "this does not look well."

But, when the dressing was finished, the wounded man moved his fingers, opened his mouth, then his eyes, cast around him troubled, haggard glances, then appeared to search about in his memory, to recollect, to understand, and he murmured:

"Ah! good God! this has done for me!"

The doctor held his hand.

"Why no, why no, some days of rest merely — it will be nothing."

Hautot returned:

"It has done for me! My stomach is split open! I know it well."

Then, all of a sudden:

"I want to talk to the son, if I have the time."

Hautot Junior, in spite of himself, shed tears, and kept repeating like a little boy:

"P'pa, p'pa, poor p'pa!"

But the father, in a firmer tone:

"Come! stop crying — this is not the time for it. I have to talk to you. Sit down there quite close to me. It will be quickly done, and I shall be more calm. As for the rest of you, kindly give me one minute."

They all went out, leaving the father and son face to face.

As soon as they were alone:

"Listen, son! you are twenty-four years; one can say things like this to you. And then there is not such mystery about these matters as we import into them. You know well that your mother has been seven years dead, isn't that so? and that I am not more than forty-five years myself, seeing that I got married at nineteen? Is not that true?"

The son faltered:

"Yes, it is true."

"So then your mother has been seven years dead, and I have remained a widower. Well! a man like me cannot remain without a wife at thirty-eight, isn't that true?"

The son replied:

"Yes, it is true."

The father, out of breath, quite pale, and his face contracted with suffering, went on:

"God! what pain I feel! Well, you understand. Man is not made to live alone, but I did not want to take a successor to your mother, since I promised her not to do so. Then — you understand?"

"Yes, father."

"So, I kept a young girl at Rouen, Rue d'Éperlan 18, in the third story, the second door, — I tell you all this, don't forget, — but a young girl, who has been very nice to me, — loving, devoted, a true woman, eh? You comprehend, my lad?"

"Yes, father."

"So then, if I am carried off, I owe something to her, something substantial, that will place her in a safe position. You understand?"

"Yes, father."

"I tell you that she is an honest girl, and that, but for you, and the remembrance of your mother, and again but for the house in which we three lived, I would have brought her here, and then married her, for certain — listen — listen, my lad. I might have made a will — I haven't done so. I did not wish to do so — for it is not necessary to write down things — things of this sort — it is too hurtful to the legitimate children — and then it embroils everything — it ruins everyone! Look you, the stamped paper, there's no need of it — never make use of it. If I am rich, it is because I have not made waste of what I have during my own life. You understand, my son?"

"Yes, father."

"Listen again — listen well to me! So then, I have made no will — I did not desire to do so — and then I knew what you were; you have a good heart; you are not niggardly, not too near, in any way; I said to myself that when my end approached I would tell you all about it, and that I would beg of you not to forget the girl. And then listen again! When I am gone, make your way to the place at once — and make such arrangements that she may not blame my memory. You have plenty of means. I leave it to you — I leave you enough. Listen! You won't find her at home every day in the week. She works at Madame Moreau's in the Rue Beauvoisine. Go there on a Thursday. That is the day she expects me. It has been my day for the past six years. Poor little thing! she will weep! — I say all this to you because I have known you so well, my son. One does not tell these things in public either to the notary or to the priest. They happen — everyone knows that — but they are not talked about, save in case of necessity. Then there is no outsider in the secret, nobody except the family, because the family consists of one person alone. You understand?"

"Yes, father."

"Do you promise?"

"Yes, father."

"Do you swear it?"

"Yes, father."

"I beg of you, I implore of you, so do not forget. I bind you to it."

"No, father."

"You will go yourself. I want you to make sure of everything."

"Yes, father."

"And, then, you will see—you will see what she will explain to you. As for me, I can say no more to you. You have vowed to do it."

"Yes, father."

"That's good, my son. Embrace me. Farewell. I am going to break up, I'm sure. Tell them they may come in."

Young Hautot embraced his father, groaning while he did so; then, always docile, he opened the door, and the priest appeared in a white surplice, carrying the holy oils.

But the dying man had closed his eyes and he refused to open them again, he refused to answer, he refused to show, even by a sign, that he understood.

He had spoken enough, this man; he could speak no more. Besides he now felt his heart calm; he wanted to die in peace. What need had he to make a confession to the deputy of God, since he had just done so to his son, who constituted his own family?

He received the last rites, was purified and absolved, in the midst of his friends and his servants on their bended knees, without any movement of his face indicating that he still lived.

He expired about midnight, after four hours' convulsive movements, which showed that he must have suffered dreadfully in his last moments.

II.

It was on the following Tuesday that they buried him; the shooting had opened on Sunday. On his return home, after having accompanied his father to the cemetery, César Hautot spent the rest of the day weeping. He scarcely slept at all on the following night, and he felt so sad on awakening that he asked himself how he could go on living.

However, he kept thinking until evening that, in order to obey the last wish of his father, he ought to repair to Rouen next day, and see this girl Catholine Donet, who resided in the Rue d'Eperlan in the third story, second door. He had repeated to himself in a whisper, just as a little boy repeats a prayer, this name and address a countless number of times, so that he might not forget them, and he ended by lisping them continually, without being able to stop or to think of what they were, so much were his tongue and his mind possessed by the commission.

Accordingly, on the following day, about eight o'clock, he ordered Graindorge to be yoked to the tilbury, and set forth at the quick trotting pace of the heavy Norman horse, along the highroad from Ainville to Rouen. He wore his black frock-coat, a tall silk hat on his head, and breeches with straps; and he did not, on account of the occasion, dispense with the handsome costume, the blue overalls which swelled in the wind, protecting the cloth from dust and from stains, and which was to be removed quickly the moment he jumped out of the coach.

He entered Rouen accordingly just as it was striking ten o'clock, drew up, as he had usually done, at
the Hôtel des Bon-Enfants, in the Rue des Trois-
Marcs, submitted to the hugs of the landlord and his
wife and their five children, for they had heard the
melancholy news. After that, he had to tell them all
the particulars about the accident, which caused him
to shed tears, to repel all the proffered attentions
which they sought to thrust upon him merely because he was wealthy, and to decline even the breakfast they wanted him to partake of, thus wounding
their sensibilities.

Then, having wiped the dust off his hat, brushed
his coat and removed the mud stains from his boots,
he set forth in search of the Rue d'Eperlan, without venturing to make inquiries from anyone, for fear
of being recognized and arousing suspicions.

At length, being unable to find the place, he saw
a priest passing by, and, trusting to the professional
discretion which churchmen possess, he questioned
the ecclesiastic.

He had only a hundred steps farther to go; it was
exactly the second street to the right.

Then he hesitated. Up to that moment, he had
obeyed, like a mere animal, the expressed wish of the
deceased. Now he felt quite agitated, confused, humiliated, at the idea of finding himself—the son—
in the presence of this woman who had been his
father's mistress. All the morality which lies buried
in our breasts, heaped up at the bottom of our sen-
suous emotions by centuries of hereditary instruction,
all that he had been taught, since he had learned his
catechism, about creatures of evil life, the instinctive

contempt which every man entertains for them, even though he may marry one of them, all the narrow honesty of the peasant in his character, was stirred up within him and held him back, making him grow red with shame.

But he said to himself:

"I promised the father, I must not break my promise."

Then he gave a push to the door of the house bearing the number 18, which stood ajar, discovered a gloomy-looking staircase, ascended three flights, perceived a door, then a second door, came upon the string of a bell, and pulled it. The ringing, which resounded in the apartment before which he stood, sent a shiver through his frame. The door was opened, and he found himself facing a young lady very well dressed, a brunette with a fresh complexion, who gazed at him with eyes of astonishment.

He did not know what to say to her, and she, who suspected nothing, and who was waiting for him to speak, did not invite him to come in. They stood looking thus at one another for nearly half a minute, at the end of which she said in a questioning tone:

"You have something to tell me, Monsieur?"

He falteringly replied:

"I am M. Hautot's son."

She gave a start, turned pale, and stammered out as if she had known him for a long time:

"Monsieur César?"

"Yes."

"And what next?"

"I have come to speak to you on the part of my father."

She articulated:

"Oh, my God!"

She then drew back so that he might enter. He shut the door and followed her into the interior. Then he saw a little boy of four or five years playing with a cat, seated on the floor in front of a stove, from which rose the steam of dishes which were being kept hot.

"Take a seat," she said.

He sat down.

She asked:

"Well?"

He no longer ventured to speak, keeping his eyes fixed on the table which stood in the center of the room, with three covers laid on it, one of which was for a child. He glanced at the chair which had its back turned to the fire. They had been expecting him. That was his bread which he saw, and which he recognized near the fork, for the crust had been removed on account of Hautot's bad teeth. Then, raising his eyes, he noticed on the wall his father's portrait, the large photograph taken at Paris the year of the exhibition, the same as that which hung above the bed in the sleeping apartment at Ainville.

The young woman again asked:

"Well, Monsieur César?"

He kept staring at her. Her face was livid with anguish; and she waited, her hands trembling with fear.

Then he took courage.

"Well, Mam'zelle, papa died on Sunday last just after he had opened the shooting."

She was so much overwhelmed that she did not move. After a silence of a few seconds, she faltered in an almost inaudible tone:

"Oh! it is not possible!"

Then, on a sudden, tears showed themselves in her eyes, and covering her face with her hands, she burst out sobbing.

At that point the little boy turned round, and, see-ing his mother weeping, began to howl. Then, re-alizing that this sudden trouble was brought about by the stranger, he rushed at César, caught hold of his breeches with one hand and with the other hit him with all his strength on the thigh. And César remained agitated, deeply affected, with this woman mourning for his father at one side of him, and the little boy defending his mother at the other. He felt their emotion taking possession of himself, and his eyes were beginning to brim over with the same sorrow; so, to recover his self-command, he began to talk:

"Yes," he said, "the accident occurred on Sunday, at eight o'clock—"

And he told, as if she were listening to him, all the facts without forgetting a single detail, mention-ing the most trivial matters with the minuteness of a countryman. And the child still kept assailing him, making kicks at his ankles.

When he came to the time at which his father had spoken about her, her attention was caught by hearing her own name, and, uncovering her face, she said:

"Pardon me! I was not following you; I would like to know—if you do not mind beginning over again."

He related everything at great length, with stoppages, breaks, and reflections of his own from time to time.   She listened to him eagerly now perceiving with a woman's keen sensibility all the sudden changes of fortune which his narrative indicated, and trembling with horror, every now and then, exclaiming:

"Oh, my God!"

The little fellow, believing that she had calmed down, ceased beating César, in order to catch his mother's hand, and he listened, too, as if he understood.

When the narrative was finished, young Hautot continued:

"Now, we will settle matters together in accordance with his wishes. Listen: I am well off, he has left me plenty of means. I don't want you to have anything to complain about—"

But she quickly interrupted him:

"Oh! Monsieur César, Monsieur César, not to-day. I am cut to the heart—another time—another day. No, not to-day. If I accept, listen! 'Tis not for myself—no, no, no, I swear to you. 'Tis for the child. Besides this provision will be put to his account."

Thereupon César scared, divined the truth, and stammering:

"So then—'tis his—the child?"

"Why, yes," she said.

And Hautot Junior gazed at his brother with a confused emotion, intense and painful.

After a lengthened silence, for she had begun to weep afresh, César, quite embarrassed, went on:

"Well, then, Mam'zelle Donet, I am going. When would you wish to talk this over with me?"

She exclaimed:

"Oh! no, don't go! don't go! Don't leave me all alone with Emile. I would die of grief. I have no longer anyone, anyone but my child. Oh! what wretchedness, what wretchedness. Monsieur César! Stop! Sit down again. You will say something more to me. You will tell me what he was doing over there all the week."

And César resumed his seat, accustomed to obey.

She drew over another chair for herself in front of the stove, where the dishes had all this time been simmering, took Emile upon her knees, and asked César a thousand questions about his father with reference to matters of an intimate nature, which made him feel, without reasoning on the subject, that she had loved Hautot with all the strength of her frail woman's heart.

And, by the natural concatenation of his ideas — which were rather limited in number — he recurred once more to the accident, and set about telling the story over again with all the same details.

When he said: "He had a hole in his stomach — you could put your two fists into it," she gave vent to a sort of shriek, and the tears gushed forth again from her eyes.

Then, seized by the contagion of her grief, César began to weep, too, and as tears always soften the fibers of the heart, he bent over Emile whose forehead was close to his own mouth and kissed him.

The mother, recovering her breath, murmured:

"Poor lad, he is an orphan now!"

"And so am I," said César.

And they ceased to talk.

But suddenly the practical instinct of the house-wife, accustomed to be thoughtful about many things, revived in the young woman's breast.

"You have perhaps taken nothing all the morning, Monsieur César."

"No, Mam'zelle."

"Oh! you must be hungry. You will eat a morsel."

"Thanks," he said, "I am not hungry; I have had too much trouble."

She replied:

"In spite of sorrow, we must live. You will not refuse to let me get something for you! And then you will remain a little longer. When you are gone I don't know what will become of me."

He yielded after some further resistance, and, sitting down with his back to the fire, facing her, he ate a plateful of tripe, which had been bubbling in the stove, and drank a glass of red wine. But he would not allow her to uncork the bottle of white wine. He several times wiped the mouth of the little boy, who had smeared all his chin with sauce.

As he was rising up to go, he asked:

"When would you like me to come back to speak about this business to you, Mam'zelle Donet?"

"If it is all the same to you, say next Thursday, Monsieur César. In that way I would lose none of my time, as I always have my Thursdays free."

"That will suit me—next Thursday."

"You will come to lunch. Won't you?"

"Oh! On that point I can't give you a promise."

"The reason I suggested it is that people can chat better when they are eating. One has more time, too."

"Well, be it so. About twelve o'clock, then."

And he took his departure, after he had again kissed little Emile, and pressed Mademoiselle Donet's hand.

III.

The week appeared long to César Hautot. He had never before found himself alone, and the isolation seemed to him insupportable. Till now, he had lived at his father's side, just like his shadow, followed him into the fields, superintended the execution of his orders, and, when they had been a short time separated, again met him at dinner. They had spent the evenings smoking their pipes, face to face with one another, chatting about horses, cows, or sheep, and the grip of their hands when they rose up in the morning might have been regarded as a manifestation of deep family affection on both sides.

Now César was alone, he went vacantly through the process of dressing the soil in autumn, every moment expecting to see the tall gesticulating silhouette of his father rising up at the end of a plain. To kill time, he entered the houses of his neighbors, told about the accident to all who had not heard of it, and sometimes repeated it to the others. Then, after he had finished his occupations and his reflections, he would sit down at the side of the road, asking himself whether this kind of life was going to last forever.

He frequently thought of Mademoiselle Donet. He liked her. He considered her thoroughly respectable, a gentle and honest young woman, as his father had

said. Yes, undoubtedly she was an honest girl. He
resolved to act handsomely toward her, and to give
her two thousand francs a year, settling the capital
on the child. He even experienced a certain pleasure
in thinking that he was going to see her on the following Thursday and arrange this matter with her.
And then the notion of this brother, this little chap
of five, who was his father's son, plagued him, annoyed him a little, and at the same time, excited
him. He had, as it were, a family in this brat,
sprung from a clandestine alliance, who would never
bear the name of Hautot, a family which he might
take or leave, just as he pleased, but which would
recall his father.

And so, when he saw himself on the road to
Rouen on Thursday morning, carried along by Graindorge trotting with clattering foot-beats, he felt his
heart lighter, more at peace than he had hitherto felt
it since his bereavement.

On entering Mademoiselle Donet's apartment, he
saw the table laid as on the previous Thursday, with
the sole difference that the crust had not been removed from the bread. He pressed the young
woman's hand, kissed Emile on the cheeks, and sat
down, more or less as if he were in his own house,
his heart swelling in the same way. Mademoiselle
Donet seemed to him a little thinner and paler. She
must have grieved sorely. She wore now an air of
constraint in his presence, as if she understood what
she had not felt the week before under the first blow
of her misfortune, and she exhibited an excessive deference toward him, a mournful humility, and made
touching efforts to please him, as if to pay him back

by her attentions for the kindness he had manifested
toward her. They were a long time at lunch talking
over the business which had brought him there.
She did not want so much money. It was too much.
She earned enough to live on herself, but she only
wished that Emile might find a few sous awaiting
him when he grew big. César held out, however,
and even added a gift of a thousand francs for herself for the expense of mourning.

When he had taken his coffee, she asked:

"Do you smoke?"

"Yes—I have my pipe."

He felt in his pocket. Good God! He had forgotten it! He was becoming quite woe-begone about
it when she offered him a pipe of his father's that had
been shut up in a cupboard. He accepted it, took it
up in his hand, recognized it, smelled it, spoke of its
quality in a tone of emotion, filled it with tobacco,
and lighted it. Then he set Emile astride on his
knee, and made him play the cavalier, while she removed the tablecloth and put the soiled plates at
one end of the sideboard in order to wash them as
soon as he was gone.

About three o'clock, he rose up with regret, quite
annoyed at the thought of having to go.

"Well! Mademoiselle Donet," he said, "I wish you
good evening, and am delighted to have found you
like this."

She remained standing before him, blushing, much
affected, and gazed at him while she thought of the
other.

"Shall we not see one another again?" she said.

He replied simply:

"Why, yes, Mam'zelle, if it gives you pleasure."

"Certainly, Monsieur César. Will next Thursday suit you then?"

"Yes, Mademoiselle Donet."

"You will come to lunch, of course?"

"Well—if you are so kind as to invite me, I can't refuse."

"It is understood, then, Monsieur César—next Thursday, at twelve, the same as to-day."

"Thursday at twelve, Mam'zelle Donet!"

NO QUARTER

THE broad sunlight threw its burning rays on the fields, and under this shower of flame life burst forth in glowing vegetation from the earth. As far as the eye could see, the soil was green; and the sky was blue to the verge of the horizon. The Norman farms scattered through the plain seemed at a distance like little woods inclosed each in a circle of thin beech-trees. Coming closer, on opening the worm-eaten stile, one fancied that he saw a giant garden, for all the old apple-trees, as knotted as the peasants, were in blossom. The weather-beaten black trunks, crooked, twisted, ranged along the inclosure, displayed beneath the sky their glittering domes, rosy and white. The sweet perfume of their blossoms mingled with the heavy odors of the open stables and with the fumes of the steaming dunghill, covered with hens and their chickens. It was midday. The family sat at dinner in the shadow of the pear-tree planted before the door — the father, the mother, the four children, the two maidservants, and the three farm laborers. They

(40)

scarcely uttered a word. Their fare consisted of soup and of a stew composed of potatoes mashed up in lard.

From time to time one of the maidservants rose up, and went to the cellar to fetch a pitcher of cider.

The husband, a big fellow of about forty, stared at a vine-tree, quite exposed to view, which stood close to the farmhouse, twining like a serpent under the shutters the entire length of the wall.

He said, after a long silence:

" The father's vine-tree is blossoming early this year. Perhaps it will bear good fruit."

The peasant's wife also turned round, and gazed at the tree without speaking.

This vine-tree was planted exactly in the place where the father of the peasant had been shot.

It was during the war of 1870. The Prussians were in occupation of the entire country. General Faidherbe, with the Army of the North, was at their head.

Now the Prussian staff had taken up its quarters in this farmhouse. The old peasant who owned it, Père Milon, received them, and gave them the best treatment he could.

For a whole month the German vanguard remained on the lookout in the village. The French were posted ten leagues away without moving, and yet, each night, some of the uhlans disappeared.

All the isolated scouts, those who were sent out on patrol, whenever they started in groups of two or three, never came back.

They were picked up dead in the morning in a
field, near a farmyard, in a ditch. Their horses even
were found lying on the roads with their throats cut
by a saber stroke. These murders seemed to have
been accomplished by the same men, who could not
be discovered.

The country was terrorized. Peasants were shot
on mere information, women were imprisoned, at-
tempts were made to obtain revelations from children
by fear.

But, one morning, Père Milon was found stretched
in his stable with a gash across his face.

Two uhlans ripped open were seen lying three
kilometers away from the farmhouse. One of them
still grasped in his hand his blood-stained weapon.
He had fought and defended himself.

A council of war having been immediately constituted, in the open air, in front of the farmhouse,
the old man was brought before it.

He was sixty-eight years old. He was small, thin,
a little crooked, with long hands resembling the claws
of a crab. His faded hair, scanty and slight, like the
down on a young duck, allowed his scalp to be
plainly seen. The brown, crimpled skin of his neck
showed the big veins which sank under his jaws and
reappeared at his temples. He was regarded in the
district as a miser and a hard man in business transactions.

He was placed standing between four soldiers in
front of the kitchen table, which had been carried out
of the house for the purpose. Five officers and the
Colonel sat facing him. The Colonel was the first to
speak.

"Père Milon," he said, in French, "since we came here we have had nothing to say of you but praise. You have always been obliging, and even considerate toward us. But to-day a terrible accusation rests on you, and the matter must be cleared up. How did you get the wound on your face?"

The peasant gave no reply.

The Colonel went on:

"Your silence condemns you, Père Milon. But I want you to answer me, do you understand? Do you know who has killed the two uhlans who were found this morning near the crossroads?"

The old man said in a clear voice:

"It was I!"

The Colonel, surprised, remained silent for a second, looking steadfully at the prisoner. Père Milon maintained his impassive demeanor, his air of rustic stupidity, with downcast eyes, as if he were talking to his curé. There was only one thing that could reveal his internal agitation, the way in which he slowly swallowed his saliva with a visible effort, as if he were choking.

The old peasant's family — his son Jean, his daughter-in-law, and two little children stood ten paces behind, scared and dismayed.

The Colonel continued:

"Do you know also who killed all the scouts of our army whom we have found every morning, for the past month, lying here and there in the fields?"

The old man answered with the same brutal impassiveness:

"It was I!"

"It is you, then, that killed them all?"

"All of them — yes, it was I."

"You alone?"

"I alone."

"Tell me the way you managed to do it?"

This time the peasant appeared to be affected; the necessity of speaking at some length incommoded him.

"I know myself. I did it the way I found easiest."

The Colonel proceeded:

"I warn you, you must tell me everything. You will do well, therefore, to make up your mind about it at once. How did you begin it?"

The peasant cast an uneasy glance toward his family, who remained in a listening attitude behind him. He hesitated for another second or so, then all of a sudden he came to a resolution on the matter.

"I came home one night about ten o'clock, and the next day you were here. You and your soldiers gave me fifty crowns for forage with a cow and two sheep. Said I to myself: 'As long as I get twenty crowns out of them, I'll sell them the value of it.' But then I had other things in my heart, which I'll tell you about now. I came across one of your cavalrymen smoking his pipe near my dike, just behind my barn. I went and took my scythe off the hook, and I came back with short steps from behind, while he lay there without hearing anything. And I cut off his head with one stroke, like a feather, while he only said 'Oof!' You have only to look at the bottom of the pond; you'll find him there in a coal bag with a big stone tied to it.

"I got an idea into my head. I took all he had on him from his boots to his cap, and I hid them in the bakehouse in the Martin wood behind the farm-yard."

The old man stopped. The officers, speechless, looked at one another. The examination was re-sumed, and this is what they were told.

Once he had accomplished this murder, the peas-ant lived with only one thought: "To kill the Prussians!" He hated them with the sly and fero-cious hatred of a countryman who was at the same time covetous and patriotic. He had got an idea into his head, as he put it. He waited for a few days.

He was allowed to go and come freely, to go out and return just as he pleased, as long as he displayed humility, submissiveness, and complaisance toward the conquerors.

Now, every evening he saw the cavalrymen bear-ing dispatches leaving the farmhouse; and he went out, one night, after discovering the name of the village to which they were going, and after picking up by associating with the soldiers the few words of German he needed.

He made his way through his farmyard, slipped into the wood, reached the bakehouse, penetrated to the end of the long passage, and having found the clothes of the soldier which he had hidden there, he put them on. Then he went prowling about the fields, creeping along, keeping to the slopes so as to avoid observation, listening to the least sounds, rest-less as a poacher.

When he believed the time had arrived he took up his position at the roadside, and hid himself in a clump of brushwood. He still waited. At length, near midnight, he heard the galloping of a horse's hoofs on the hard soil of the road. The old man put his ear to the ground to make sure that only one cavalryman was approaching; then he got ready.

The uhlan came on at a very quick pace, carrying some dispatches. He rode forward with watchful eyes and strained ears. As soon as he was no more than ten paces away, Père Milon dragged himself across the road, groaning: "Hilfe! hilfe!" ("Help! help!").

The cavalryman drew up, recognized a German soldier dismounted, believed that he was wounded, leaped down from his horse, drew near the prostrate man, never suspecting anything, and, as he stooped over the stranger, he received in the middle of the stomach the long, curved blade of the saber. He sank down without any death throes, merely quivering with a few last shudders.

Then the Norman, radiant with the mute joy of an old peasant, rose up, and merely to please himself, cut the dead soldier's throat. After that, he dragged the corpse to the dike and threw it in.

The horse was quietly waiting for its rider. Père Milon got on the saddle and started across the plain at the gallop.

At the end of an hour, he perceived two more uhlans approaching the staff-quarters side by side. He rode straight toward them, crying: "Hilfe! hilfe!" The Prussians let him come on, recognizing the uniform without any distrust.

And like a cannon ball the old man shot between the two, bringing both of them to the ground with his saber and a revolver. The next thing he did was to cut the throats of the horses — the German horses! Then, softly he re-entered the bakehouse and hid the horse he had ridden himself in the dark passage. There he took off the uniform, put on once more his own old clothes, and going to his bed, slept till morning.

For four days, he did not stir out, awaiting the close of the open inquiry as to the cause of the soldiers' deaths; but, on the fifth day, he started out again, and by a similar stratagem killed two more soldiers.

Thenceforth, he never stopped. Each night he wandered about, prowled through the country at random, cutting down some Prussians, sometimes here, sometimes there, galloping through the deserted fields under the moonlight, a lost uhlan, a hunter of men. Then, when he had finished his task, leaving behind him corpses lying along the roads, the old horseman went to the bakehouse where he concealed both the animal and the uniform. About midday he calmly returned to the spot to give the horse a feed of oats and some water, and he took every care of the animal, exacting therefore the hardest work.

But, the night before his arrest, one of the soldiers he attacked put himself on his guard, and cut the old peasant's face with a slash of a saber.

He had, however, killed both of them. He had even managed to go back and hide his horse and put on his everyday garb, but, when he reached the stable, he was overcome by weakness and was not able to make his way into the house.

He had been found lying on the straw, his face covered with blood.

When he had finished his story, he suddenly lifted his head and glanced proudly at the Prussian officers.

The Colonel, tugging at his mustache, asked:

"Have you anything more to say?"

"No, nothing more; we are quits. I killed sixteen, not one more, not one less."

"You know you have to die?"

"I ask for no quarter!"

"Have you been a soldier?"

"Yes, I served at one time. And 'tis you killed my father, who was a soldier of the first Emperor, not to speak of my youngest son François, whom you killed last month near Exreux. I owed this to you, and I've paid you back. 'Tis tit for tat!"

The officers stared at one another.

The old man went on:

"Eight for my father, eight for my son — that pays it off! I sought for no quarrel with you. I don't know you! I only know where you came from. You came to my house here and ordered me about as if the house was yours. I have had my revenge, and I'm glad of it!"

And stiffening up his old frame, he folded his arms in the attitude of a humble hero.

The Prussians held a long conference. A captain, who had also lost a son the month before defended the brave old farmer.

Then the Colonel rose up, and, advancing toward Père Milon, he said, lowering his voice:

"Listen, old man! There is perhaps one way of saving your life — it is — "

But the old peasant was not listening to him, and, fixing his eyes directly on the German officer, while

the wind made the scanty hair move to and fro on
his skull, he made a frightful grimace, which shriv-
eled up his pinched countenance scarred by the
saber-stroke, and, puffing out his chest, he spat, with
all his strength, right into the Prussian's face.

The Colonel, stupefied, raised his hand, and for
the second time the peasant spat in his face.

All the officers sprang to their feet and yelled out
orders at the same time.

In less than a minute the old man, still as impassive as ever, was stuck up against the wall and
shot, while he cast a smile at Jean, his eldest son,
and then at his daughter-in-law and the two children,
who were staring with terror at the scene.

THE ORPHAN

MADEMOISELLE SOURCE had adopted this boy under very sad circumstances. She was at the time thirty-six years old. She was disfigured, having in her infancy slipped off her nurse's lap into the fireplace, and getting her face so shockingly burned that it ever afterward presented a frightful appearance. This deformity had made her resolve not to marry, for she did not want any man to marry her for her money.

A female neighbor of hers, being left a widow during her pregnancy, died in childbirth, without leaving a sou. Mademoiselle Source took the newborn child, put him out to nurse, reared him, sent him to a boarding-school, then brought him home in his fourteenth year, in order to have in her empty house somebody who would love her, who would look after her, who would make her old age pleasant.

She resided on a little property four leagues away from Rennes, and she now dispensed with a servant.

The expenses having increased to more than double what they had been since this orphan's arrival, her income of three thousand francs was no longer sufficient to support three persons.

She attended to the housekeeping and the cooking herself, and sent the boy out on errands, letting him further occupy himself with cultivating the garden. He was gentle, timid, silent, and caressing. And she experienced a deep joy, a fresh joy at being embraced by him, without any apparent surprise or repugnance being exhibited by him on account of her ugliness. He called her "Aunt" and treated her as a mother.

In the evening they both sat down at the fireside, and she got nice things ready for him. She heated some wine and toasted a slice of bread, and it made a charming little meal before going to bed. She often took him on her knees and covered him with kisses, murmuring in his ear with passionate tenderness. She called him: "My little flower, my cherub, my adored angel, my divine jewel." He softly accepted her caresses, concealing his head on the old maid's shoulder. Although he was now nearly fifteen years old, he had remained small and weak, and had a rather sickly appearance.

Sometimes Mademoiselle Source brought him to the city to see two married female relatives of hers, distant cousins, who were living in the suburbs, and who were the only members of her family in existence. The two women had always found fault with her for having adopted this boy, on account of the inheritance; but for all that they gave her a cordial welcome, having still hopes of getting a share for themselves, a third, no doubt, if what she possessed were only equally divided.

She was happy, very happy, always taken up with her adopted child. She bought books for him to improve his mind, and he devoted himself ardently to reading.

He no longer now climbed on her knees to fondle her as he had formerly done; but instead would go and sit down in his little chair in the chimney-corner and open a volume. The lamp placed at the edge of the little table, above his head, shone on his curly hair and on a portion of his forehead; he did not move, he did not raise his eyes, he did not make any gesture. He read on, interested, entirely absorbed in the adventures which formed the subject of the book.

She, seated opposite to him, gazed at him with an eager, steady look, astonished at his studiousness, jealous, often on the point of bursting into tears.

She said to him now and then: "You will fatigue yourself, my treasure!" in the hope that he would raise his head and come across to embrace her; but he did not even answer her; he had not heard or understood what she was saying; he paid no attention to anything save what he read in these pages.

For two years he devoured an incalculable number of volumes. His character changed.

After this, he asked Mademoiselle Source many times for money, which she gave him. As he always wanted more, she ended by refusing, for she was both regular and energetic and knew how to act rationally when it was necessary to do so. By dint of entreaties he obtained a large sum one night from her; but when he urged her to give him another

sum a few days later, she showed herself inflexible,
and did not give way to him further, in fact.

He appeared to be satisfied with her decision.

He again became quiet, as he had formerly been,
loving to remain seated for entire hours, without
moving, plunged in deep reverie. He now did not
even talk to Madame Source, merely answering her
remarks with short, formal words. Nevertheless, he
was agreeable and attentive in his manner toward
her; but he never embraced her now.

She had by this time grown slightly afraid of him
when they sat facing one another at night at opposite
sides of the fireplace. She wanted to wake him
up, to make him say something, no matter what,
that would break this dreadful silence, which was
like the darkness of a wood. But he did not appear
to listen to her, and she shuddered with the terror of
a poor feeble woman when she had spoken to him
five or six times successively without being able to
get a word out of him.

What was the matter with him? What was going
on in that closed-up head? When she had been thus
two or three hours sitting opposite him, she felt herself getting daft, and longed to rush away and to escape into the open country in order to avoid that
mute, eternal companionship and also some vague
danger, which she could not define, but of which she
had a presentiment.

She frequently shed tears when she was alone.
What was the matter with him? When she gave
expression to a desire, he unmurmuringly carried it
into execution. When she wanted to have anything
brought to her from the city, he immediately went

there to procure it. She had no complaint to make
of him; no, indeed! And yet —

Another year flitted by, and it seemed to her that
a new modification had taken place in the mind of
the young man. She perceived it; she felt it; she
divined it. How? No matter! She was sure she
was not mistaken; but she could not have explained
in what the unknown thoughts of this strange youth
had changed.

It seemed to her that till now he had been like a
person in a hesitating frame of mind who had suddenly arrived at a determination. This idea came to
her one evening as she met his glance, a fixed, singular glance which she had not seen in his face before.

Then he commenced to watch her incessantly,
and she wished she could hide herself in order to
avoid that cold eye, riveted on her.

He kept staring at her, evening after evening for
hours together, only averting his eyes when she said,
utterly unnerved:

"Do not look at me like that, my child!"

Then he bowed his head.

But the moment her back was turned, she once
more felt that his eye was upon her. Wherever she
went he pursued her with his persistent gaze.

Sometimes, when she was walking in her little
garden, she suddenly noticed him squatted on the
stump of a tree as if he were lying in wait for her;
and again when she sat in front of the house mend-
ing stockings while he was digging some cabbage-
bed, he kept watching her, as he worked, in a sly,
continuous fashion.

It was in vain that she asked him:

"What's the matter with you, my boy? For the last three years, you have become very different. I don't find you the same. Tell me what ails you, and what you are thinking of, I beg of you."

He invariably replied, in a quiet, weary tone:

"Why, nothing ails me, Aunt!"

And when she persisted, appealing to him thus: "Ah! my child, answer me, answer me when I speak to you. If you knew what grief you caused me, you would always answer, and you would not look at me that way. Have you any trouble? Tell me, I'll console you!" he would turn away with a tired air, murmuring:

"But there is nothing the matter with me, I assure you."

He had not grown much, having always a childish aspect, although the features of his face were those of a man. They were, however, hard and badly cut. He seemed incomplete, abortive, only half finished, and disquieting as a mystery. He was a close impenetrable being, in whom there seemed always to be some active, dangerous mental travail taking place.

Mademoiselle Source was quite conscious of all this, and she could not, from that time forth, sleep at night, so great was her anxiety. Frightful terrors, dreadful nightmares assailed her. She shut herself up in her own room and barricaded the door, tortured by fear.

What was she afraid of? She could not tell.

Fear of everything, of the night, of the walls, of the shadows thrown by the moon on the white curtains of the windows, and, above all, fear of him.

Why? What had she to fear? Did she know what it was? She could live this way no longer! She felt certain that a misfortune threatened her, a frightful misfortune.

She set forth secretly one morning and went into the city to see her relatives. She told them about the matter in a gasping voice. The two women thought she was going mad and tried to reassure her.

She said:

"If you knew the way he looks at me from morning till night. He never takes his eyes off me! At times I feel a longing to cry for help, to call in the neighbors, so much am I afraid. But what could I say to them? He does nothing to me except to keep looking at me."

The two female cousins asked:

"Is he ever brutal to you? Does he give you sharp answers?"

She replied:

"No, never; he does everything I wish; he works hard; he is steady; but I am so frightened I don't mind that much. He has something in his head, I am certain of that — quite certain. I don't care to remain all alone like that with him in the country."

The relatives, scared by her words, declared to her that they were astonished and could not understand her; and they advised her to keep silent about her fears and her plans, without, however, dissuading her from coming to reside in the city, hoping in that way that the entire inheritance would eventually fall into their hands.

They even promised to assist her in selling her house and in finding another near them.

Mademoiselle Source returned home. But her mind was so much upset that she trembled at the slightest noise, and her hands shook whenever any trifling disturbance agitated her.

Twice she went again to consult her relatives, quite determined now not to remain any longer in this way in her lonely dwelling. At last she found a little cottage in the suburbs, which suited her, and privately she bought it.

The signature of the contract took place on a Tuesday morning, and Mademoiselle Source devoted the rest of the day to the preparations for her change of residence.

At eight o'clock in the evening she got into the diligence which passed within a few hundred yards of her house, and she told the conductor to let her down in the place where it was his custom to stop for her. The man called out to her as he whipped his horses:

"Good evening, Mademoiselle Source — good night!"

She replied as she walked on:

"Good evening, Père Joseph." Next morning, at half past seven, the postman who conveyed letters to the village, noticed at the crossroad, not far from the highroad, a large splash of blood not yet dry. He said to himself: "Hallo! some boozer must have been bleeding from the nose."

But he perceived ten paces farther on a pocket-handkerchief also stained with blood. He picked them up. The linen was fine, and the postman, in alarm, made his way over to the dike, where he fancied he saw a strange object.

Mademoiselle Source was lying at the foot on the grass, her throat cut open with a knife.

An hour later, the gendarmes, the examining magistrate, and other authorities made an inquiry as to the cause of death.

The two female relatives, called as witnesses, told all about the old maid's fears and her last plans.

The orphan was arrested. Since the death of the woman who had adopted him, he wept from morning till night, plunged, at least to all appearance, in the most violent grief.

He proved that he had spent the evening up to eleven o'clock in a *café*. Ten persons had seen him, having remained there till his departure.

Now the driver of the diligence stated that he had set down the murdered woman on the road between half past nine and ten o'clock.

The accused was acquitted. A will, a long time made, which had been left in the hands of a notary in Rennes, made him universal legatee. So he inherited everything.

For a long time the people of the country put him into quarantine, as they still suspected him. His house, which was that of the dead woman, was looked upon as accursed. People avoided him in the street.

But he showed himself so good-natured, so open, so familiar, that gradually these horrible doubts were forgotten. He was generous, obliging, ready to talk to the humblest about anything as long as they cared to talk to him.

The notary, Maître Rameay, was one of the first to take his part, attracted by his smiling loquacity.

He said one evening at a dinner at the tax-collector's house:

"A man who speaks with such facility and who is always in good-humor could not have such a crime on his conscience."

Touched by this argument, the others who were present reflected, and they recalled to mind the long conversations with this man who made them stop almost by force at the road corners to communicate his ideas to them, who insisted on their going into his house when they were passing by his garden, who could crack a joke better than the lieutenant of the gendarmes himself, and who possessed such contagious gaiety that, in spite of the repugnance with which he inspired them, they could not keep from always laughing when in his company.

All doors were opened to him after a time.

He is, to-day, the mayor of his own community.

A LIVELY FRIEND

THEY had been constantly in each other's society for a whole winter in Paris. After having lost sight of each other, as generally happens in such cases, after leaving college, the two friends met again one night, long years after, already old and white-haired, the one a bachelor, the other married.

M. de Meroul lived six months in Paris and six months in his little château at Tourbeville. Having married the daughter of a gentleman in the district, he had lived a peaceful, happy life with the indolence of a man who has nothing to do. With a calm temperament and a sedate mind, without any intellectual audacity or tendency toward revolutionary independence of thought, he passed his time in mildly regretting the past, in deploring the morals and the institutions of to-day, and in repeating every moment to his wife, who raised her eyes to heaven, and sometimes her hands also, in token of energetic assent:

(60)

"Under what a government do we live, great God!"

Madame de Meroul mentally resembled her husband, just as if they had been brother and sister. She knew by tradition that one ought, first of all, to reverence the Pope and the King!

And she loved them and respected them from the bottom of her heart, without knowing them, with a poetic exaltation, with a hereditary devotion, with all the sensibility of a well-born woman. She was kindly in every feeling of her soul. She had no child, and was incessantly regretting it.

When M. de Meroul came across his old school-fellow Joseph Mouradour at a ball, he experienced from this meeting a profound and genuine delight, for they had been very fond of one another in their youth.

After exclamations of astonishment over the changes caused by age in their bodies and their faces, they had asked one another a number of questions as to their respective careers.

Joseph Mouradour, a native of the south of France, had become a councillor-general in his own neighborhood. Frank in his manners, he spoke briskly and without any circumspection, telling all his thoughts with sheer indifference to prudential considerations. He was a Republican, of that race of good-natured Republicans who make their own ease the law of their existence, and who carry freedom of speech to the verge of brutality.

He called at his friend's address in Paris, and was immediately a favorite, on account of his easy cordiality, in spite of his advanced opinions. Madame de Meroul exclaimed:

"What a pity! such a charming man!"

M. de Meroul said to his friend, in a sincere and confidential tone: "You cannot imagine what a wrong you do to our country." He was attached to his friend nevertheless, for no bonds are more solid than those of childhood renewed in later life. Joseph Mouradour chaffed the husband and wife, called them "my loving turtles," and occasionally gave vent to loud declarations against people who were behind the age, against all sorts of prejudices and traditions.

When he thus directed the flood of his democratic eloquence, the married pair, feeling ill at ease, kept silent through a sense of propriety and good-breeding; then the husband tried to turn off the conversation in order to avoid any friction. Joseph Mouradour did not want to know anyone unless he was free to say what he liked.

Summer came round. The Merouls knew no greater pleasure than to receive their old friends in their country house at Tourbeville. It was an intimate and healthy pleasure, the pleasure of homely gentlefolk who had spent most of their lives in the country. They used to go to the nearest railway station to meet some of their guests, and drove them to the house in their carriage, watching for compliments on their district, on the rapid vegetation, on the condition of the roads in the department, on the cleanliness of the peasants' houses, on the bigness of the cattle they saw in the fields, on everything that met the eye as far as the edge of the horizon.

They liked to have it noticed that their horse trotted in a wonderful manner for an animal employed

a part of the year in field-work; and they awaited
with anxiety the newcomer's opinion on their family
estate, sensitive to the slightest word, grateful for the
slightest gracious attention.

Joseph Mouradour was invited, and he announced
his arrival. The wife and the husband came to meet
the train, delighted to have the opportunity of doing
the honors of their house.

As soon as he perceived them, Joseph Mouradour
jumped out of his carriage with a vivacity which increased their satisfaction. He grasped their hands
warmly, congratulated them, and intoxicated them
with compliments.

He was quite charming in his manner as they
drove along the road to the house; he expressed astonishment at the height of the trees, the excellence
of the crops, and the quickness of the horse.

When he placed his foot on the steps in front of
the château, M. de Meroul said to him with a certain
friendly solemnity:

"Now you are at home."

Joseph Mouradour answered: "Thanks, old fellow;
I counted on that. For my part, besides, I never put
myself out with my friends. That's the only hos-
pitality I understand."

Then he went up to his own room, where he
put on the costume of a peasant, as he was pleased
to describe it, and he came down again not very
long after, attired in blue linen, with yellow boots,
in the careless rig-out of a Parisian out for a holiday.
He seemed, too, to have become more common,
more jolly, more familiar, having assumed along with
his would-be rustic garb a free and easy swagger

which he thought suited the style of dress. His new apparel somewhat shocked M. and Madame de Meroul, who even at home on their estate always remained serious and respectable, as the particle "de" before their name exacted a certain amount of ceremonial even with their intimate friends.

After lunch they went to visit the farms; and the Parisian stupefied the respectable peasants by talking to them as if he were a comrade of theirs.

In the evening, the curé dined at the house — a fat old priest, wearing his Sunday suit, who had been specially asked that day in order to meet the newcomer.

When Joseph saw him he made a grimace, then he stared at the priest in astonishment as if he belonged to some peculiar race of beings, the like of which he had never seen before at such close quarters. He told a few stories allowable enough with a friend after dinner, but apparently somewhat out of place in the presence of an ecclesiastic. He did not say, "Monsieur l'Abbé," but merely "Monsieur"; and he embarrassed the priest with philosophical views as to the various superstitions that prevailed on the surface of the globe.

He remarked:

"Your God, Monsieur, is one of those persons whom we must respect, but also one of those who must be discussed. Mine is called Reason; he has from time immemorial been the enemy of yours."

The Merouls, greatly put out, attempted to divert his thoughts. The curé left very early.

Then the husband gently remarked:

"You went a little too far with that priest."

But Joseph immediately replied:

"That's a very good joke, too! Am I to bother my brains about a devil-dodger? At any rate, do me the favor of not ever again having such an old fogy to dinner. Confound his impudence!"

"But, my friend, remember his sacred character."

Joseph Mouradour interrupted him:

"Yes, I know. We must treat them like girls who get roses for being well behaved! That's all right, my boy! When these people respect my convictions, I will respect theirs!"

This was all that happened that day.

Next morning Madame de Meroul, on entering her drawing-room, saw lying on the table three newspapers which made her draw back in horror, "Le Voltaire," "La République Française," and "La Justice."

Presently Joseph Mouradour, still in his blue blouse, appeared on the threshold, reading "L' Intransigéant" attentively. He exclaimed:

"Here is a splendid article by Rochefort. That fellow is marvelous."

He read the article in a loud voice, laying so much stress on its most striking passages that he did not notice the entrance of his friend.

M. de Meroul had a paper in each hand: "Le Gaulois" for himself and "Le Clarion" for his wife.

The ardent prose of the master-writer who overthrew the empire, violently declaimed, recited in the accent of the south, rang through the peaceful drawing-room, shook the old curtains with their rigid folds, seemed to splash the walls, the large upholstered chairs, the solemn furniture fixed in the same position for the past century, with a hail of words, rebounding, impudent, ironical, and crushing.

The husband and the wife, the one standing, the other seated, listened in a state of stupor, so scandalized that they no longer even ventured to make a gesture. Mouradour flung out the concluding passage in the article as one sets off a stream of fireworks; then in an emphatic tone he remarked:

"That's a stinger, eh?"

But suddenly he perceived the two prints belonging to his friend, and he seemed himself for a moment overcome with astonishment. Then he came across to his host with great strides, demanding in an angry tone:

"What do you want to do with these papers?"

M. de. Meroul replied in a hesitating voice:

"Why, these — these are my — my newspapers."

"Your newspapers! Look here, now, you are only laughing at me! You will do me the favor to read mine, to stir you up with a few new ideas, and, as for yours — this is what I do with them —"

And before his host, filled with confusion, could prevent him, he seized the two newspapers and flung them out through the window. Then he gravely placed "La Justice" in the hands of Madame de Meroul and "Le Voltaire" in those of her husband, himself sinking into an armchair to finish "L'Intransigéant."

The husband and the wife, through feelings of delicacy, made a show of reading a little, then they handed back the Republican newspapers which they touched with their finger-tips as if they had been poisoned.

Then Mouradour burst out laughing, and said:

"A week of this sort of nourishment, and I'll have you converted to my ideas."

At the end of a week, in fact, he ruled the house. He had shut the door on the curé, whom Madame de Meroul went to see in secret. He gave orders that neither the "Gaulois" nor the "Clarion" were to be admitted into the house, which a manservant went to get in a mysterious fashion at the post-office, and which, on his entrance, were hidden away under the sofa cushions. He regulated everything just as he liked, always charming, always good-natured, a jovial and all-powerful tyrant.

Other friends were about to come on a visit, religious people with Legitimist opinions. The master and mistress of the château considered it would be impossible to let them meet their lively guest, and not knowing what to do, announced to Joseph Mouradour one evening that they were obliged to go away from home for a few days about a little matter of business, and they begged of him to remain in the house alone.

He showed no trace of emotion, and replied:

"Very well; 'tis all the same to me; I'll wait here for you as long as you like. What I say is this — there need be no ceremony between friends. You're quite right to look after your own affairs — why the devil shouldn't you? I'll not take offense at your doing that, quite the contrary. It only makes me feel quite at my ease with you. Go, my friends — I'll wait for you."

M. and Madame de Meroul started next morning.

He is waiting for them.

THE BLIND MAN

How is it that the sunlight gives us such joy? Why does this radiance when it falls on the earth fill us so much with the delight of living? The sky is all blue, the fields are all green, the houses all white; and our ravished eyes drink in those bright colors which bring mirthfulness to our souls. And then there springs up in our hearts a desire to dance, a desire to run, a desire to sing, a happy lightness of thought, a sort of enlarged tenderness; we feel a longing to embrace the sun.

The blind, as they sit in the doorways, impassive in their eternal darkness, remain as calm as ever in the midst of this fresh gaiety, and, not comprehending what is taking place around them, they continue every moment to stop their dogs from gamboling.

When, at the close of the day, they are returning home on the arm of a young brother or a little sister, if the child says: "It was a very fine day!" the other answers: "I could notice that 'twas fine. Lulu wouldn't keep quiet."

(68)

I have known one of these men whose life was one of the most cruel martyrdoms that could possibly be conceived.

He was a peasant, the son of a Norman farmer. As long as his father and mother lived, he was more or less taken care of; he suffered little save from his horrible infirmity; but as soon as the old people were gone, a life of atrocious misery commenced for him. A dependent on a sister of his, everybody in the farmhouse treated him as a beggar who is eating the bread of others. At every meal the very food he swallowed was made a subject of reproach against him; he was called a drone, a clown; and although his brother-in-law had taken possession of his portion of the inheritance, the soup was given to him grudgingly—just enough to save him from dying.

His face was very pale and his two big white eyes were like wafers. He remained unmoved in spite of the insults inflicted upon him, so shut up in himself that one could not tell whether he felt them at all.

Moreover, he had never known any tenderness; his mother had always treated him very unkindly, caring scarcely at all for him; for in country places the useless are obnoxious, and the peasants would be glad, like hens, to kill the infirm of their species.

As soon as the soup had been gulped down, he went to the door in summer time and sat down, to the chimney-corner in winter time, and, after that, never stirred till night. He made no gesture, no movement; only his eyelids, quivering from some nervous affection, fell down sometimes over his white sightless orbs. Had he any intellect, any thinking

faculty, any consciousness of his own existence?
Nobody cared to inquire as to whether he had
or no.

For some years things went on in this fashion.
But his incapacity for doing anything as well as his
impassiveness eventually exasperated his relatives, and
he became a laughing-stock, a sort of martyred buf-
foon, a prey given over to native ferocity, to the savage gaiety of the brutes who surrounded him.

It is easy to imagine all the cruel practical jokes
inspired by his blindness. And, in order to have
some fun in return for feeding him, they now converted his meals into hours of pleasure for the neighbors and of punishment for the helpless creature
himself.

The peasants from the nearest houses came to this
entertainment; it was talked about from door to door,
and every day the kitchen of the farmhouse was full
of people. For instance, they put on the table in
front of his plate, when he was beginning to take
the soup, a cat or a dog. The animal instinctively
scented out the man's infirmity, and, softly approaching, commenced eating noiselessly, lapping up the
soup daintily; and, when a rather loud licking of the
tongue awakened the poor fellow's attention, it would
prudently scamper away to avoid the blow of the
spoon directed at it by the blind man at random!

Then the spectators, huddled against the walls,
burst out laughing, nudged each other, and stamped
their feet on the floor. And he, without ever uttering a word, would continue eating with the aid of
his right hand, while stretching out his left to protect
and defend his plate.

At another time they made him chew corks, bits of wood, leaves, or even filth, which he was unable to distinguish.

After this, they got tired even of these practical jokes; and the brother-in-law, mad at having to support him always, struck him, cuffed him incessantly, laughing at the useless efforts of the other to ward off or return the blows. Then came a new pleasure —the pleasure of smacking his face. And the plowmen, the servant-girls, and even every passing vagabond were every moment giving him cuffs, which caused his eyelashes to twitch spasmodically. He did not know where to hide himself and remained with his arms always held out to guard against people coming too close to him.

At last he was forced to beg.

He was placed somewhere on the highroad on market-days, and, as soon as he heard the sound of footsteps or the rolling of a vehicle, he reached out his hat, stammering:

"Charity, if you please!"

But the peasant is not lavish, and, for whole weeks, he did not bring back a sou.

Then he became the victim of furious, pitiless hatred. And this is how he died.

One winter, the ground was covered with snow, and it froze horribly. Now his brother-in-law led him one morning at this season a great distance along the highroad in order that he might solicit alms. The blind man was left there all day, and, when night came on, the brother-in-law told the people of his house that he could find no trace of the mendicant. Then he added:

"Pooh! best not bother about him! He was cold, and got some one to take him away. Never fear! he's not lost. He'll turn up soon enough to-morrow to eat the soup."

Next day he did not come back.

After long hours of waiting, stiffened with the cold, feeling that he was dying, the blind man began to walk. Being unable to find his way along the road, owing to its thick coating of ice, he went on at random, falling into dikes, getting up again, without uttering a sound, his sole object being to find some house where he could take shelter.

But by degrees the descending snow made a numbness steal over him, and his feeble limbs being incapable of carrying him farther, he had to sit down in the middle of an open field. He did not get up again.

The white flakes which kept continually falling buried him, so that his body, quite stiff and stark, disappeared under the incessant accumulation of their rapidly thickening mass; and nothing any longer indicated the place where the corpse was lying.

His relatives made pretense of inquiring about him and searching for him for about a week. They even made a show of weeping.

The winter was severe, and the thaw did not set in quickly. Now, one Sunday, on their way to mass, the farmers noticed a great flight of crows, who were whirling endlessly above the open field, and then, like a shower of black rain, descended in a heap at the same spot, ever going and coming.

The following week these gloomy birds were still there. There was a crowd of them up in the air, as if they had gathered from all corners of the horizon; and they swooped down with a great cawing into the shining snow, which they filled curiously with patches of black, and in which they kept rummaging obstinately. A young fellow went to see what they were doing, and discovered the body of the blind man, already half devoured, mangled. His wan eyes had disappeared, pecked out by the long voracious beaks.

And I can never feel the glad radiance of sunlit days without sadly remembering and gloomily pondering over the fate of the beggar so deprived of joy in life that his horrible death was a relief for all those who had known him.

THE IMPOLITE SEX

MADAME DE X. TO MADAME DE L.

ETRETAT, Friday.

MY DEAR AUNT,—I am going to pay you a visit without making much fuss about it. I shall be at Les Fresnes on the second of September, the day before the hunting season opens; I do not want to miss it, so that I may tease these gentlemen. You are very obliging, Aunt, and I would like you to allow them to dine with you, as you usually do when there are no strange guests, without dressing or shaving for the occasion, on the ground that they are fatigued.

They are delighted, of course, when I am not present. But I shall be there, and I shall hold a review, like a general, at the dinner-hour; and, if I find a single one of them at all careless in dress, no matter how little, I mean to send him down to the kitchen to the servant-maids.

(74)

The men of to-day have so little consideration for others and so little good manners that one must be always severe with them. We live indeed in an age of vulgarity. When they quarrel with one another, they attack one another with insults worthy of street porters, and, in our presence, they do not conduct themselves even as well as our servants. It is at the seaside that you see this most clearly. They are to be found there in battalions, and you can judge them in the lump. Oh, what coarse beings they are!

Just imagine, in a train, one of them, a gentleman who looked well as I thought, at first sight, thanks to his tailor, was dainty enough to take off his boots in order to put on a pair of old shoes! Another, an old man, who was probably some wealthy upstart (these are the most ill-bred), while sitting opposite to me, had the delicacy to place his two feet on the seat quite close to me. This is a positive fact.

At the watering-places, there is an unrestrained outpouring of unmannerliness. I must here make one admission — that my indignation is perhaps due to the fact that I am not accustomed to associate as a rule with the sort of people one comes across here, for I should be less shocked by their manners if I had the opportunity of observing them oftener. In the inquiry-office of the hotel I was nearly thrown down by a young man, who snatched the key over my head. Another knocked against me so violently without begging my pardon or lifting his hat, coming away from a ball at the Casino, that he gave me a pain in the chest. It is the same way with all of them. Watch them addressing ladies on the terrace:

they scarcely ever bow. They merely raise their
hands to their headgear. But indeed, as they are all
more or less bald, it is the best plan.

But what exasperates and disgusts me especially
is the liberty they take of talking publicly, without
any precaution whatsoever, about the most revolting
adventures. When two men are together, they re-
late to each other, in the broadest language and with
the most abominable comments, really horrible stories,
without caring in the slightest degree whether a
woman's ear is within reach of their voices. Yesterday, on the beach, I was forced to go away from
the place where I sat in order not to be any longer
the involuntary confidant of an obscene anecdote,
told in such immodest language that I felt as much
humiliated as I was indignant at having heard it.
Would not the most elementary good-breeding have
taught them to speak in a lower tone about such
matters when we are near at hand? Etretat is, moreover, the country of gossip and scandal. From five
to seven o'clock you can see people wandering about
in quest of nasty stories about others, which they re-
tail from group to group. As you remarked to me,
my dear Aunt, tittle-tattle is the mark of petty individuals and petty minds. It is also the consolation
of women who are no longer loved or sought after.
It is enough for me to observe the women who are
fondest of gossiping to be persuaded that you are
quite right.

The other day I was present at a musical evening
at the Casino, given by a remarkable artist, Madame
Masson, who sings in a truly delightful manner. I
took the opportunity of applauding the admirable

Coquelin, as well as two charming boarders of the Vaudeville, M—— and Meillet.   I was able, on the occasion, to see all the bathers collected together this year on the beach.   There were not many persons of distinction among them.

One day I went to lunch at Yport.   I noticed a tall man with a beard who was coming out of a large house like a castle.   It was the painter, Jean Paul Laurens.   He is not satisfied apparently with imprisoning the subjects of his pictures; he insists on imprisoning himself.

Then I found myself seated on the shingle close to a man still young, of gentle and refined appearance, who was reading some verses.   But he read them with such concentration, with such passion, I may say, that he did not even raise his eyes toward me. I was somewhat astonished, and I asked the conductor of the baths, without appearing to be much concerned, the name of this gentleman.   I laughed inwardly a little at this reader of rhymes: he seemed behind the age, for a man.   This person, I thought, must be a simpleton.   Well, Aunt, I am now infatuated about this stranger.   Just fancy, his name is Sully Prudhomme!   I turned round to look at him at my ease, just where I sat.   His face possesses the two qualities of calmness and elegance.   As somebody came to look for him, I was able to hear his voice, which is sweet and almost timid.   He would certainly not tell obscene stories aloud in public, or knock against ladies without apologizing.   He is sure to be a man of refinement, but his refinement is of an almost morbid, vibrating character.   I will try this winter to get an introduction to him.

I have no more news to tell you, my dear Aunt, and I must interrupt this letter in haste, as the post-hour is near. I kiss your hands and your cheeks. Your devoted niece,   BERTHE DE X.

P.S.—I should add, however, by way of justification of French politeness, that our fellow-countrymen are, when traveling, models of good manners in comparison with the abominable English, who seem to have been brought up by stable-boys, so much do they take care not to incommode themselves in any way, while they always incommode their neighbors.

MADAME DE L. TO MADAME DE X.

LES FRESNES, Saturday.

MY DEAR CHILD,—Many of the things you have said to me are very reasonable, but that does not prevent you from being wrong. Like you, I used formerly to feel very indignant at the impoliteness of men, who, as I supposed, constantly treated me with neglect; but, as I grew older and reflected on everything, putting aside coquetry and observing things without taking any part in them myself, I perceived this much—that if men are not always polite, women are always indescribably rude.

We imagine that we should be permitted to do anything, my darling, and at the same time we consider that we have a right to the utmost respect, and in the most flagrant manner we commit actions devoid of that elementary good-breeding of which you speak with passion.

I find, on the contrary, that men have, for us, much consideration, as compared with our bearing toward them. Besides, darling, men must needs be, and are, what we make them. In a state of society where women are all true gentlewomen all men would become gentlemen.

Mark my words; just observe and reflect.

Look at two women meeting in the street. What an attitude each assumes toward the other! What disparaging looks! What contempt they throw into each glance! How they toss their heads while they inspect each other to find something to condemn! And, if the footpath is narrow, do you think one woman will make room for another, or will beg pardon as she sweeps by? Never! When two men jostle each other by accident in some narrow lane, each of them bows and at the same time gets out of the other's way, while we women press against each other, stomach to stomach, face to face, insolently staring each other out of countenance.

Look at two women who are acquaintances meeting on a staircase before the drawing-room door of a friend of theirs to whom one has just paid a visit, and to whom the other is about to pay a visit. They begin to talk to each other, and block up the passage. If anyone happens to be coming up behind them, man or woman, do you imagine that they will put themselves half an inch out of their way? Never! never!

I was waiting myself, with my watch in my hands, one day last winter, at a certain drawing-room door. Behind me two gentlemen were also waiting without showing any readiness to lose their temper, like me. The reason was that they had long grown accustomed to our unconscionable insolence.

The other day, before leaving Paris, I went to dine with no less a person than your husband in the Champs-Elysées, in order to enjoy the open air. Every table was occupied. The waiter asked us not to go, and there would soon be a vacant table.

At that moment, I noticed an elderly lady of noble figure, who, having paid the amount of her check, seemed on the point of going away. She saw me, scanned me from head to foot, and did not budge. For more than a full quarter of an hour she sat there, immovable, putting on her gloves, and calmly staring at those who were waiting like myself. Now, two young men who were just finishing their dinner, having seen me in their turn, quickly summoned the waiter in order to pay whatever they owed, and at once offered me their seats, even insisting on standing while waiting for their change. And, bear in mind, my fair niece, that I am no longer pretty, like you, but old and white-haired.

It is we (do you see?) who should be taught politeness; and the task would be such a difficult one that Hercules himself would not be equal to it. You speak to me about Etretat, and about the people who indulge in "tittle-tattle" along the beach of that delightful watering-place. It is a spot now lost to me, a thing of the past, but I found much amusement there in days gone by.

There were only a few of us, people in good society, really good society, and a few artists, and we all fraternized. We paid little attention to gossip in those days.

Well, as we had no insipid Casino, where people only gather for show, where they talk in whispers, where they dance stupidly, where they succeed in thoroughly boring one another, we sought some other way of passing our evenings pleasantly. Now, just guess what came into the head of one of our husbandry? Nothing less than to go and dance each night in one of the farmhouses in the neighborhood.

We started out in a group with a street-organ, generally played by Le Poittevin, the painter, with a cotton nightcap on his head. Two men carried lanterns. We followed in procession, laughing and chattering like a pack of fools.

We woke up the farmer and his servant-maids and laboring men. We got them to make onion-soup (horror!), and we danced under the apple-trees, to the sound of the barrel-organ. The cocks waking up began to crow in the darkness of the outhouses; the horses began prancing on the straw of their stables. The cool air of the country caressed our cheeks with the smell of grass and of new-mown hay.

How long ago it is! How long ago it is. It is thirty years since then!

I do not want you, my darling, to come for the opening of the hunting season. Why spoil the pleasure of our friends by inflicting on them fashionable toilettes after a day of vigorous exercise in the country? This is the way, child, that men are spoiled. I embrace you.

Your old aunt,　　GENEVIEVE DE L.

THE CAKE

L ET us say that her name was Madame
Anserre so as not to reveal her real
name.

She was one of those Parisian comets
which leave, as it were, a trail of fire
behind them. She wrote verses and
novels; she had a poetic heart, and
was rarely beautiful. She opened her
doors to very few — only to exceptional
people, those who are commonly described as princes of something or other.

To be a visitor at her house constituted
a claim, a genuine claim to intellect: at least
this was the estimate set on her invitations.

Her husband played the part of an obscure satel-
lite. To be the husband of a comet is not an easy
thing. This husband had, however, an original idea,
that of creating a State within a State, of possessing
a merit of his own, a merit of the second order, it is
true; but he did, in fact, in this fashion, on the days
when his wife held receptions, hold receptions also
on his own account. He had his special set who ap-
preciated him, listened to him, and bestowed on him
more attention than they did on his brilliant partner.

(82)

He had devoted himself to agriculture — to agriculture in the Chamber. There are in the same way generals in the Chamber — those who are born, who live, and who die, on the round leather chairs of the War Office, are all of this sort, are they not? Sailors in the Chamber, — viz., in the Admiralty, — colonizers in the Chamber, etc., etc. So he had studied agriculture, had studied it deeply, indeed, in its relations to the other sciences, to political economy, to the Fine Arts — we dress up the Fine Arts with every kind of science, and we even call the horrible railway bridges "works of art." At length he reached the point when it was said of him: "He is a man of ability." He was quoted in the technical reviews; his wife had succeeded in getting him appointed a member of a committee at the Ministry of Agriculture.

This latest glory was quite sufficient for him.

Under the pretext of diminishing the expenses, he sent out invitations to his friends for the day when his wife received hers, so that they associated together, or rather did not — they formed two distinct groups. Madame, with her escort of artists, academicians, and ministers, occupied a kind of gallery, furnished and decorated in the style of the Empire. Monsieur generally withdrew with his agriculturists into a smaller portion of the house used as a smoking-room and ironically described by Madame Anserre as the Salon of Agriculture.

The two camps were clearly separate. Monsieur, without jealousy, moreover, sometimes penetrated into the Academy, and cordial hand-shakings were exchanged; but the Academy entertained infinite con-

tempt for the Salon of Agriculture, and it was rarely
that one of the princes of science, of thought, or of
anything else, mingled with the agriculturists.

These receptions occasioned little expense — a cup
of tea, a cake, that was all. Monsieur, at an earlier
period, had claimed two cakes, one for the Academy,
and one for the agriculturists, but Madame having
rightly suggested that this way of acting seemed to
indicate two camps, two receptions, two parties,
Monsieur did not press the matter, so that they used
only one cake, of which Madame Anserre did the
honors at the Academy, and which then passed into
the Salon de Agriculture.

Now, this cake was soon, for the Academy, a
subject of observation well calculated to arouse curiosity. Madame Anserre never cut it herself. That
function always fell to the lot of one or other of the
illustrious guests. The particular duty, which was
supposed to carry with it honorable distinction, was
performed by each person for a pretty long period,
in one case for three months, scarcely ever for more;
and it was noticed that the privilege of "cutting the
cake" carried with it a heap of other marks of supe-
riority — a sort of royalty, or rather very accentuated
viceroyalty.

The reigning cutter spoke in a haughty tone, with
an air of marked command; and all the favors of the
mistress of the house were for him alone.

These happy individuals were in moments of intimacy described in hushed tones behind doors as the
"favorites of the cake," and every change of favorite
introduced into the Academy a sort of revolution.
The knife was a scepter, the pastry an emblem; the

chosen ones were congratulated. The agriculturists never cut the cake. Monsieur himself was always excluded, although he ate his share.

The cake was cut in succession by poets, by painters, and by novelists. A great musician had the privilege of measuring the portions of the cake for some time; an ambassador succeeded him. Sometimes a man less well known, but elegant and sought after, one of those who are called according to the different epochs, "true gentleman," or "perfect knight," or "dandy," or something else, seated himself, in his turn, before the symbolic cake. Each of them, during this ephemeral reign, exhibited greater consideration toward the husband; then, when the hour of his fall had arrived, he passed on the knife toward the other, and mingled once more with the crowd of followers and admirers of the "beautiful Madame Anserre."

This state of things lasted a long time; but comets do not always shine with the same brilliance. Everything gets worn out in society. One would have said that gradually the eagerness of the cutters grew feebler; they seemed to hesitate at times when the tray was held out to them; this office, once so much coveted, became less and less desired. It was retained for a shorter time; they appeared to be less proud of it.

Madame Anserre was prodigal of smiles and civilities. Alas! no one was found any longer to cut it voluntarily. The newcomers seemed to decline the honor. The "old favorites" reappeared one by one like dethroned princes who have been replaced for a brief spell in power. Then, the chosen ones became

few, very few. For a month (oh, prodigy!) M.
Anserre cut open the cake; then he looked as if he
were getting tired of it; and one evening Madame
Anserre, the beautiful Madame Anserre, was seen
cutting it herself. But this appeared to be very
wearisome to her, and, next day, she urged one of
her guests so strongly to do it that he did not dare
to refuse.

The symbol was too well known, however; the
guests stared at one another with scared, anxious
faces. To cut the cake was nothing, but the privileges to which this favor had always given a claim
now frightened people; therefore, the moment the
dish made its appearance the academicians rushed
pellmell into the Salon of Agriculture, as if to shelter
themselves behind the husband, who was perpetually
smiling. And when Madame Anserre, in a state of
anxiety, presented herself at the door with a cake in
one hand and the knife in the other, they all seemed
to form a circle around her husband as if to appeal
to him for protection.

Some years more passed. Nobody cut the cake
now; but yielding to an old inveterate habit, the
lady who had always been gallantly called "the
beautiful Madame Anserre" looked out each evening
for some devotee to take the knife, and each time
the same movement took place around her, a general
flight, skillfully arranged and full of combined maneuvers that showed great cleverness, in order to
avoid the offer that was rising to her lips.

But, one evening, a young man presented himself
at her reception — an innocent, unsophisticated youth.
He knew nothing about the mystery of the cake;

accordingly, when it appeared, and when all the rest
ran away, when Madame Anserre took from the manservant's hands the dish and the pastry, he remained
quietly by her side.

She thought that perhaps he knew about the matter; she smiled, and in a tone which showed some
emotion, said:

"Will you be kind enough, dear Monsieur, to cut
this cake?"

He displayed the utmost readiness, and took off
his gloves, flattered at such an honor being conferred
on him.

"Oh, to be sure, Madame, with the greatest pleasure."

Some distance away in the corner of the gallery,
in the frame of the door which led into the Salon
of the Agriculturists, faces which expressed utter
amazement were staring at him. Then, when the
spectators saw the newcomer cutting without any
hesitation, they quickly came forward.

An old poet jocosely slapped the neophyte on the
shoulder.

"Bravo, young man!" he whispered in his ear.

The others gazed at him with curiosity. Even the
husband appeared to be surprised. As for the young
man, he was astonished at the consideration which
they suddenly seemed to show toward him; above
all, he failed to comprehend the marked attentions,
the manifest favor, and the species of mute gratitude
which the mistress of the house bestowed on him.

It appears, however, that he eventually found out.

At what moment, in what place, was the revela-
tion made to him? Nobody could tell; but, when he

again presented himself at the reception, he had a preoccupied air, almost a shamefaced look, and he cast around him a glance of uneasiness.

The bell rang for tea. The manservant appeared. Madame Anserre, with a smile, seized the dish, casting a look about her for her young friend; but he had fled so precipitately that no trace of him could be seen any longer. Then, she went looking everywhere for him, and ere long she discovered him in the Salon of the Agriculturists. With his arm locked in that of the husband, he was consulting that gentleman as to the means employed for destroying phylloxera.

"My dear Monsieur," she said to him, "will you be so kind as to cut this cake for me?"

He reddened to the roots of his hair, and hanging down his head, stammered out some excuses. Thereupon M. Anserre took pity on him, and turning toward his wife, said:

"My dear, you might have the goodness not to disturb us. We are talking about agriculture. So get your cake cut by Baptiste."

And since that day nobody has ever cut Madame Anserre's cake.

THE CORSICAN BANDIT

THE road, with a gentle winding, reached the middle of the forest. The huge pine-trees spread above our heads a mournful-looking vault, and gave forth a kind of long, sad wail, while at either side their straight, slender trunks formed, as it were, an army of organ-pipes, from which seemed to issue the low, monotonous music of the wind through the tree-tops.

After three hours' walking there was an opening in this row of tangled branches. Here and there an enormous pine-parasol, separated from the others, opening like an immense umbrella, displayed its dome of dark green; then, all of a sudden, we gained the boundary of the forest, some hundreds of meters below the defile which leads into the wild valley of Niolo.

On the two projecting heights which commanded a view of this pass, some old trees, grotesquely twisted, seemed to have mounted with painful efforts, like scouts who had started in advance of the multitude heaped together in the rear. When we turned round we saw the entire forest stretched beneath our feet, like a gigantic basin of verdure, whose edges, which seemed to reach the sky, were composed of bare racks shutting in on every side.

We resumed our walk, and, ten minutes later, we found ourselves in the defile.

Then I beheld an astonishing landscape. Beyond another forest, a valley, but a valley such as I had never seen before, a solitude of stone ten leagues long, hollowed out between two high mountains, without a field or a tree to be seen. This was the Niolo valley, the fatherland of Corsican liberty, the inaccessible citadel, from which the invaders had never been able to drive out the mountaineers.

My companion said to me: "It is here, that all our bandits have taken refuge."

Ere long we were at the further end of this chasm, so wild, so inconceivably beautiful.

Not a blade of grass, not a plant—nothing but granite. As far as our eyes could reach we saw in front of us a desert of glittering stone, heated like an oven by a burning sun which seemed to hang for that very purpose right above the gorge. When we raised our eyes toward the crests we stood dazzled and stupefied by what we saw. They looked red and notched like festoons of coral, for all the summits are made of porphyry; and the sky overhead seemed violet, lilac, discolored by the vicinity of these strange mountains. Lower down the granite was of scintillating gray, and under our feet it seemed rasped, pounded; we were walking over shining powder. At our right, along a long and irregular course, a tumultuous torrent ran with a continuous roar. And we staggered along under this heat, in this light, in this burning, arid, desolate valley cut by this ravine of turbulent water which seemed to be ever hurrying onward, without being able to fertilize these rocks, lost in this furnace which greedily drank it up without being penetrated or refreshed by it.

But suddenly there was visible at our right a little wooden cross sunk in a little heap of stones. A man had been killed there; and I said to my companion:

"Tell me about your bandits."

He replied:

"I knew the most celebrated of them, the terrible St. Lucia. I will tell you his history.

"His father was killed in a quarrel by a young man of the same district, it is said; and St. Lucia was left alone with his sister. He was a weak and timid youth, small, often ill, without any energy. He did not proclaim the *vendetta* against the assassin of his father. All his relatives came to see him, and implored of him to take vengeance; he remained deaf to their menaces and their supplications.

"Then, following the old Corsican custom, his sister, in her indignation, carried away his black clothes, in order that he might not wear mourning for a dead man who had not been avenged. He was insensible to even this outrage, and rather than take down from the rack his father's gun, which was still loaded, he shut himself up, not daring to brave the looks of the young men of the district.

"He seemed to have even forgotten the crime, and he lived with his sister in the obscurity of their dwelling.

"But, one day, the man who was suspected of having committed the murder was about to get married. St. Lucia did not appear to be moved by this news; but, no doubt out of sheer bravado, the bridegroom, on his way to the church, passed before the two orphans' house.

"The brother and the sister, at their window, were eating little fried cakes when the young man saw the bridal procession moving past the house. Suddenly he began to tremble, rose up without uttering a word, made the sign of the cross, took the gun which was hanging over the fireplace, and went out.

"When he spoke of this later on, he said: 'I don't know what was the matter with me; it was like fire in my blood; I felt that I should do it, that in spite of everything, I could not resist, and I concealed the gun in a cave on the road to Corte.'

"An hour later, he came back, with nothing in his hand, and with his habitual sad air of weariness. His sister believed that there was nothing further in his thoughts.

"But when night fell he disappeared.

"His enemy had, the same evening, to repair to Corte on foot, accompanied by his two bridesmen.

"He was pursuing his way, singing as he went, when St. Lucia stood before him, and looking straight in the murderer's face, exclaimed: 'Now is the time!' and shot him point-blank in the chest.

"One of the bridesmen fled; the other stared at the young man, saying:

"'What have you done, St. Lucia?'

"Then he was going to hasten to Corte for help, but St. Lucia said in a stern tone:

"'If you move another step, I'll shoot you through the legs.'

"The other, aware that till now he had always appeared timid, said to him: 'You would not dare to do it!' and he was hurrying off when he fell, instantaneously, his thigh shattered by a bullet.

"And St. Lucia, coming over to where he lay, said:

"'I am going to look at your wound; if it is not serious, I'll leave you there; if it is mortal, I'll finish you off.'

"He inspected the wound, considered it mortal, and slowly re-loading his gun, told the wounded man to say a prayer, and shot him through the head.

"Next day he was in the mountains.

"And do you know what this St. Lucia did after this?

"All his family were arrested by the gendarmes. His uncle, the curé, who was suspected of having incited him to this deed of vengeance, was himself put into prison, and accused by the dead man's relatives. But he escaped, took a gun in his turn, and went to join his nephew in the cave.

"Next, St. Lucia killed, one after the other, his uncle's accusers, and tore out their eyes to teach the others never to state what they had seen with their eyes.

"He killed all the relatives, all the connections of his enemy's family. He massacred during his life fourteen gendarmes, burned down the houses of his adversaries, and was up to the day of his death the most terrible of the bandits, whose memory we have preserved."

*   *   *   *   *   *   *

The sun disappeared behind Monte Cinto and the tall shadow of the granite mountain went to sleep on the granite of the valley. We quickened our pace in order to reach before night the little village of Albertaccio, nothing better than a heap of stones welded beside the stone flanks of a wild gorge. And I said as I thought of the bandit:

"What a terrible custom your *vendetta* is!"

My companion answered with an air of resignation:

"What would you have? A man must do his duty!"

THE DUEL

I N SOCIETY, they called him "The handsome Signoles." He called himself Viscount Gontran Joseph de Signoles. An orphan and master of a sufficient fortune, he cut something of a figure, as the saying is. He had an attractive form, enough readiness of speech to make some attempt at wit, a certain natural grace of manner, an air of nobility and pride, and a mustache which was both formidable and pleasant to the eye — a thing that pleases the ladies.

He was in demand in drawing-rooms, sought for by waltzers, and he inspired in men that smiling enmity which one has for people of energetic physique. He was suspected of some love affairs which showed him capable of much discretion, for a young man. He lived happy, tranquil, in a state of moral well-being most complete. It was well known that he was good at handling a sword, and still better with a pistol.

"If I were to fight," he said, "I should choose a pistol. With that weapon, I am sure of killing my man."

Now, one evening, having escorted two young women, friends of his, to the theater, being also accompanied by their husbands, he offered them, after the play, an ice at Tortoni's. They had been there about ten minutes, when he perceived that a gentleman, seated at a neighboring table, gazed persistently at one of the ladies of his party. She seemed troubled and disturbed, lowering her eyes. Finally, she said to her husband:

"That man is staring me out of countenance. I do not know him; do you?"

The husband, who had seen nothing, raised his eyes but declared:

"No, not at all."

The young woman replied, half laughing, half angry: "It is very annoying; that individual is spoiling my ice."

The husband shrugged his shoulders, replying:

"Pshaw! Pay no attention to him. If we were to notice all the insolent people we meet, there would be no end to it."

But the Viscount arose brusquely. He could not allow this unknown man to spoil an ice he had offered. It was to him that the injury was addressed, as it was through him and for him that his friends had entered this *café*. The affair, then, concerned him only. He advanced toward the man and said to him:

"You have, sir, a manner of looking at these ladies that is not to be tolerated. I beg to ask you to cease this attention."

The other replied: "So you command me to keep the peace, do you?"

With set teeth, the Viscount answered: "Take care, sir, or you will force me to forget myself!"

The gentleman replied with a single word, an obscene word which resounded from one end of the *café* to the other, and made each guest start with a sudden movement as if they were all on springs. Those that were in front turned around; all the others raised their heads; three waiters turned about on their heels as if on pivots; the two ladies at the counter bounded forward, then entirely turned their backs upon the scene, as if they had been two automatons obeying the same manipulation.

There was a great silence. Then, suddenly, a sharp noise rent the air. The Viscount had struck his adversary. Everybody got up to interpose. Cards were exchanged.

After the Viscount had returned home, he walked up and down his room at a lively pace for some minutes. He was too much agitated to reflect upon anything. One idea only hovered over his mind: "a duel"; and yet this idea awoke in him as yet, no emotion whatever. He had done what he ought to do; he had shown himself what he ought to be. People would talk of it, approve of it, and congratulate him. He said aloud, in a high voice, as one speaks when he is much troubled in thought:

"What a beast that man is."

Then he sat down and began to reflect. He would have to find some seconds in the morning. Whom should he choose? He thought over the people of his acquaintance who were the most celebrated and in the best positions. He took finally, Marquis de la Tour-Noire and Colonel Bourdin, a great lord and a soldier who was very strong. Their names would carry in the journals. He perceived that he was thirsty and he drank, one after the other, three glasses of water; then he began to walk again. He felt himself full of energy. By showing himself hot-brained, resolute in all things, by exacting rigorous, dangerous conditions, and by claiming a serious duel, a very serious one, his adversary would doubtless withdraw and make some excuses.

He took up the card which he had drawn from his pocket and thrown upon the table and re-read it as he had in the *café*, by a glance of the eye, and again in the cab, on returning home, by the light of a gas jet: "George Lamil, 51 Moncey street." That was all.

He examined these assembled letters which appeared so mysterious to him, his senses all confused: George Lamil? Who was this man? What had he done? Why had he looked at that woman in such a way? Was it not revolting that a stranger, an unknown should come to trouble his life thus, at a blow, because he had been pleased to fix his insolent gaze upon a woman? And the Viscount repeated again, in a loud voice:

"What a brute."

Then he remained motionless, standing, thinking, his look ever fixed upon the card. A certain anger against this piece of paper was awakened in him, a hateful anger which was mingled with a strange sentiment of malice. It was stupid, this whole story!

He took a penknife which lay open at his hand, and pricked the card through the middle of the printed name, as if he were using a poignard upon some one.

So he must fight! Should he choose the sword or pistol, for he considered himself the insulted one. With the sword he risked less; but with the pistol, there was a chance of his adversary withdrawing. It is rarely that a duel with the sword is mortal, a reciprocal prudence hindering the combatants from keeping near enough to each other for the point to strike very deep; with the pistol he risked his life very seriously; but he could also meet the affair with all the honors of the situation and without arriving at a meeting. He said aloud:

"It is necessary to be firm. He will be afraid."

The sound of his own voice made him tremble and he began to look about him. He felt very nervous. He drank still another glass of water, then commenced to undress, preparatory to retiring.

When he was ready, he put out his light and closed his eyes. Then he thought:

"I have all day to-morrow to busy myself with my affairs. I must sleep first, in order to be calm."

He was very warm under the clothes, but he could not succeed in falling asleep. He turned and turned again, remained for five minutes upon his back, then placed himself upon his left side, then rolled over to the right.

He was still thirsty. He got up and drank. Then a kind of disquiet seized him:

"Can it be that I am afraid?" said he.

Why should his heart begin to beat so foolishly at each of the customary noises about his room? — when

14 G. de M.—20

the clock was going to strike and the spring made
that little grinding noise as it raised itself to make
the turn? And he found it was necessary for him to
open his mouth in order to breathe for some seconds
following this start, so great was his feeling of op-
pression. He began to reason with himself upon the
possibilities of the thing:

"What have I to fear?"

No, certainly, he should not fear, since he was
resolved to follow it out to the end and since he had
fully made up his mind to fight without a qualm.
But he felt himself so profoundly troubled that he
asked himself:

"Can it be that I am afraid in spite of myself?"

And this doubt invaded him, this disquiet, this
fear; if a force more powerful than his will, dominat-
ing, irresistible, should conquer him, what would
happen to him? Yes, what would happen? Certainly he could walk upon the earth, if he wished to
go there. But if he should tremble? And if he should
lose consciousness? And he thought of his situation,
of his reputation, of his name.

And a singular desire took possession of him to
get up and look at himself in the glass. He relighted
his candle. When he perceived his face reflected in
the polished glass, he scarcely knew himself, and it
seemed to him that he had never seen himself before.
His eyes appeared enormous; he was pale, certainly;
he was pale, very pale.

He remained standing there before the mirror. He
put out his tongue as if to examine the state of his
health, and suddenly this thought entered his brain
after the fashion of a bullet:

"After to-morrow at this time, I shall perhaps be dead."

And his heart began to beat furiously.

"After to-morrow at this time, I shall perhaps be dead. This person opposite me, this being I have so often seen in this glass, will be no more. How can it be! I am here, I see myself, I feel that I am alive, and in twenty-four hours I shall be stretched upon that bed, dead, my eyes closed, cold, inanimate, departed."

He turned around to the bed and distinctly saw himself stretched on his back in the same clothes he had worn on going out. In his face were the lines of death, and a rigidity in the hands that would never stir again.

Then a fear of his bed came over him, and in order to see it no more he passed into his smoking-room. Mechanically he took a cigar, lighted it, and began to walk about. He was cold. He went toward the bell to waken his valet; but he stopped with his hand on the cord:

"This man would perceive at once that I am afraid."

He did not ring, but made a fire. His hands trembled a little from a nervous shiver when they came in contact with any object. His mind wandered; his thoughts from trouble became frightened, hasty, and sorrowful; an intoxication seemed to invade his mind as if he were drunk. And without ceasing he asked:

"What am I going to do? What is going to become of me?"

His whole body was vibrating, traversed by a jerking and a trembling; he got up and approached the window, opening the curtains.

The day had dawned, a summer day. A rose-colored sky made the city rosy on roof and wall. A great fall of spread out light, like a caress from the rising sun, enveloped the waking world; and, with this light, a gay, rapid, brutal hope invaded the heart of the Viscount! He was a fool to allow himself to be thus cast down by fear, even before anything was decided, before his witnesses had seen those of this George Lamil, before he yet knew whether he were going to fight a duel.

He made his toilette, dressed himself, and walked out with firm step.

He repeated constantly, in walking:

"It will be necessary for me to be energetic, very energetic. I must prove that I am not afraid."

His witnesses, the Marquis and the Colonel, placed themselves at his disposal and, after having shaken hands with him energetically, discussed the conditions. The Colonel asked:

"Do you wish it to be a serious duel?"

The Viscount responded: "Very serious."

The Marquis continued: "Will you use a pistol?"

"Yes."

"We leave you free to regulate the rest."

The Viscount enunciated, in a dry, jerky voice:

"Twenty steps at the order, and on raising the arm instead of lowering it. Exchange of bullets until one is grievously wounded."

The Colonel declared, in a satisfied tone:

"These are excellent conditions. You shoot well, all the chances are in your favor."

They separated. The Viscount returned home to

wait for them. His agitation, appeased for a moment, grew now from minute to minute. He felt along his arms, his legs, and in his breast a kind of trembling, of continued vibration; he could not keep still, either sitting or standing. There was no longer an appearance of saliva in his mouth, and each instant he made a noisy movement with his tongue, as if to unglue it from the roof of his mouth.

He wished to breakfast but he could not eat. Then the idea came to him of drinking to give himself courage and he brought out a small bottle of rum, which he swallowed in six little glasses, one after the other.

A heat, like that of a burning fire, invaded him, followed almost immediately by a numbness of the soul. He thought:

"I have found the remedy. Now all goes well."

But at the end of an hour, he had emptied the bottle and his state of agitation became intolerable. He felt a foolish impulse to roll on the ground, to cry out and bite. Then night fell.

A stroke of the bell gave him such a shock that he had not sufficient strength left to rise and receive his witnesses. He dared not even speak to them to say "Good evening," to pronounce a single word, for fear that they would discover a change in his voice.

The Colonel announced:

" All is arranged according to the conditions that you have fixed upon. Your adversary claimed the privileges of the offended, but he soon yielded and accepted all. His witnesses are two military men."

The Viscount pronounced the word:

"Thanks."

The Marquis continued:

"Excuse us if we only come in and go out, for we have still a thousand things to occupy our attention. A good doctor will be necessary, since the combat is only to cease after a severe wound, and you know that bullets are no trifles. Then, a place must be found, in some proximity to a house, where we may carry the wounded, if necessary, etc., etc.; finally, we have but two or three hours for it."

The Viscount, for the second time, articulated:

"Thanks."

The Colonel asked:

"How is it with you? Are you calm?"

"Yes, very calm, thank you."

The two men then retired.

When he again found himself alone, it seemed to him that he was mad. His domestic having lighted the lamps, he seated himself before his table to write some letters. After having traced, at the top of a page: "This is my testament—" he arose with a shake and put it away from him, feeling himself incapable of forming two ideas, or of sufficient resolution to decide what was to be done.

So he was going to fight a duel! There was no way to avoid it. How could he ever go through it? He wished to fight, it was his intention and firm resolution so to do; and yet, he felt, that in spite of all his effort of mind and all the tension of his will, he would not be able to preserve even the necessary force to go to the place of meeting. He tried to imagine the combat, his own attitude, and the position of his adversary.

From time to time, his teeth chattered in his mouth with a little hard noise. He tried to read, and took down the Chateauvillard code of dueling. Then he asked himself:

"Has my opponent frequently fought? Is he known? Is he classed? How am I to know?"

He remembered Baron de Vaux's book upon experts with the pistol, and he ran through it from one end to the other. George Lamil was not mentioned. Nevertheless, if this man were not an expert, he would not so readily have accepted this dangerous weapon and these mortal conditions.

He opened, in passing, a box of Gastinne Renettes which stood on a little stand, took out one of the pistols, held it in a position to fire, and raised his arm. But he trembled from head to foot and the gun worked upon all his senses.

Then he said: "It is impossible. I cannot fight in this condition."

He looked at the end of the barrel, at that little black, deep hole that spits out death, he thought of the dishonor, of the whisperings in his circle, of the laughs in the drawing-rooms, of the scorn of the ladies, of the allusions of the journals, of all the insults that cowards would throw at him.

He continued to examine the weapon, and, raising the cock, he suddenly saw a priming glittering underneath like a little red flame. The pistol was loaded then, through a chance forgetfulness. And he found in this discovery a confused, inexplicable joy.

If in the presence of the other man he did not have that calm, noble bearing that he should have, he would be lost forever. He would be spotted, branded with the sign of infamy, hunted from the world! And this calm, heroic bearing he would not have, he knew it, he felt it. However, he was brave, since he did wish to fight! He was brave, since. . . . The thought that budded never took form, even in his own mind; for, opening his mouth wide he brusquely thrust the barrel of his pistol into his throat, and pulled the trigger. . . .

When his valet, hearing the report, hastened to him, he found him dead upon his back. A jet of blood had splashed upon the white paper on the table and made a great red spot upon these four words:

"This is my testament."